# Creative writing:
## *writers on writing*

Edited by
Amal Chatterjee

# Imprint information and credits

ISBN: 978-1-907076-32-9 (Paperback edition)

Published under the Creative Writing Studies imprint by
The Professional and Higher Partnership Ltd
Registered office: Suite 7, Lyndon House, 8 King's Court,
Willie Snaith Road, Newmarket, Suffolk, CB8 7SG, UK

Imprint website: creativewritingstudies.wordpress.com
Company website: http://pandhp.com

First published 2014
© Amal Chatterjee and contributors
Amal Chatterjee and the contributors assert their rights in
accordance with the Copyright, Designs and Patents Act 1988.

*Credits*
Cover image: Rika Newcombe (www.rikanewcombe.co.uk)
Cover design, text design and typesetting: Benn Linfield
  (www.bennlinfield.com)
Copy-editing: Karen Haynes
Proofreading: Elizabeth Walden
Printed by Berforts and Lightning Source

*Disclaimer*

The Professional and Higher Partnership Ltd has no responsibility for the persistence or accuracy of URLs for external or third-party websites referred to in this publication, and does not guarantee that any content on such websites is, or will remain, accurate or appropriate. The material contained in this publication is provided in good faith as general guidance. The advice and strategies contained herein may not be suitable for every situation. No liability can be accepted by The Professional and Higher Partnership Ltd for any liability, loss, risk, or damage which is incurred as a consequence, whether direct or indirect, of using or applying any of the contents of this book or the advice or guidance contained therein.

The publisher and the author make no warranties or representations with respect to the completeness or accuracy of the contents of this work and specifically disclaim all warranties, including without limitation warranties of fitness for a particular purpose. No warranty may be created or extended by sales or promotional materials.

# Series information

*Creative writing: writers on writing* is the third title to be published in the international series, Creative Writing Studies. The series comprises titles on creative writing designed for use – by scholars, students, and teachers – in higher education settings.

The first two titles in the series are:
*Rethinking creative writing in higher education*
by Stephanie Vanderslice
*Teaching creative writing: practical approaches*
edited by Elaine Walker

Further titles commissioned for the series include:
*Researching creative writing* by Jen Webb
*Studying creative writing* edited by Sharon Norris

# Contents

# Abstract

Eight original literary works, including fiction, poetry, and translation, are presented by a group of authors drawn from a variety of cultures. Each work is accompanied by a reflective commentary written by its author. The book provides three kinds of interest: (a) the literary interest of the works themselves; (b) the creative and critical interest of the commentaries' insights into the processes of writing; and (c) the pedagogic interest of the commentaries as potential models for students on creative writing courses in higher education.

# Editor's preface

Stories and poems don't just appear on a page; they germinate, grow and are crafted. So when, one evening, over another glass of wine, Anthony Haynes proposed the idea of a collection of fresh writing and essays about their creation, I jumped. After all, most of the writers I know are frequently asked about how they came up with their ideas or what motivated them to write as they do. Anthony and I discussed the idea and, the more we talked about it, the more I liked it. It would, I thought, provide writers with the opportunity to say what they really thought, what really happened when they wrote. Of course, the question was: would anyone actually want to do this? To my delight, everyone I approached agreed almost immediately, even though all couldn't join in. Most did, however, and the result is here, a collection of poetry and fiction, short stories and extracts from novels: writing, in other words, from across genres, countries and cultures, each unique and interesting, each accompanied by reflections by the authors themselves. In their own words, we have Philip Gross and Jane Draycott from the UK and Colm Breathnach from Ireland with poems, Emily Raboteau from the US, Kathryn Heyman from Australia, Sabyn Javeri from Pakistan, Fred D'Aguiar from Guyana (and the UK and the US), and myself as Indian, with original fiction, each one of us commenting on how our stories came to be, where they came from.

The first intended or imagined, though definitely not only, audience is people who want to write, who are interested in insights into the process of creation, like students and teachers of creative writing, but the book is also for anyone just interested in the process of creating fiction and poetry. The essays complement the creative writing and you can choose to read them in the sequence presented, each creation and its essay one after the other, or all the creative contributions first, then dip into the essays. You can use them to discover how we wrote, or to think about your own writing, or to encourage others, your students, whether beginners or more experienced, to consider how writing is instigated and crafted. Whichever order you read the pieces in, however you use this collection, I am sure it will give you as much pleasure and provide you with as much food for thought as it did me.

I'll borrow Fred's closing word from his essay: Enjoy.

AMAL CHATTERJEE

# About the contributors

**Colm Breathnach** was born in Cork. He is an award-winning poet and novelist. He worked as an Irish-language terminologist and as a Parliamentary translator. Now a writer and a freelance translator, he has won the principal poetry prize at the annual *Oireachtas Literary Festival* four times. In 1999, the Irish-American Cultural Institute presented him the 'Butler Literary Award'. Poems of his have been translated into English, Scottish Gaelic, German, Italian, Romanian, Chinese and Slovenian. He has been a writer-in-residence in China and in Slovenia. He has published seven collections of poetry and a novel.

**Amal Chatterjee** is the author of the novel *Across the lakes* and the non-fiction *Representations of India, 1740–1840*. He was shortlisted for the 1998 Crossword India Best Novel Award and was the recipient of a Scottish Arts Council Writer's Bursary. His short fiction has been published in *Time Out Amsterdam*, *Algebra* and *Atlas*. Born in Sri Lanka and raised in India, he is currently based in Amsterdam, writing fiction, reviewing for the Dutch newspaper *Trouw* and teaching writing, including Creative Writing at the University of Oxford.

**Fred D'Aguiar** teaches in the MFA Program at Virginia Tech. His most recent book, *Continental shelf*, a collection of poetry was a Poetry Book Society Choice and finalist for the T.S. Eliot Prize. His new collection is *The rose of Toulouse* (Carcanet, 2013).

**Jane Draycott**'s most recent collection *Over*, published by Carcanet/Oxford*Poets*, was shortlisted for the 2009 T.S. Eliot Prize. Previous collections include *Prince Rupert's drop*, *The night tree*, *No theatre* (Smith/Doorstop), and *Christina the astonishing* (with Lesley Saunders) and *Tideway* (illustrated by Peter Hay), both from Two Rivers Press. Her translation of the 14th-century *Pearl* is a Poetry Book Society Recommendation and winner of a Stephen Spender Prize. Named in 2004 as a PBS/Arts Council Next Generation poet, her work has been nominated three times for the Forward Prize for Poetry. She teaches on postgraduate writing programmes at the universities of Oxford and Lancaster.

**Philip Gross**'s *The water table* won the T.S. Eliot Prize 2009, *I spy pinhole eye* Wales Book of The Year 2010, and *Off road to everywhere* the CLPE Award for Children's Poetry 2011. His new collection, *Deep field*, a Poetry Book Society Recommendation, deals with his father's loss of language from aphasia, and with voice and language itself. He has published ten novels for young people, including *The lastling*, has written scripts, collaborated with artists, musicians and dancers, and since 2004 has been Professor of Creative Writing at Glamorgan University, where he leads the Masters in Writing programme.

**Kathryn Heyman** is the author of four novels, including *The accomplice*, and *Captain Starlight's apprentice*, published internationally and in translation. She has won an Arts Council of England Writers Award, the Wingate and the Southern Arts Awards, and been nominated for the Orange Prize, the Scottish Writer of the Year Award, the Edinburgh Fringe Critic's Awards, the Kibble Prize, and the West Australian Premier's Book Awards. She's written several radio plays for BBC radio, including adaptations of her own work, and is the Course Director for Faber Academy in Australia.

**Sabyn Javeri** was born in Karachi and lives in London. Her short stories have appeared in literary journals, *Wasafiri*, the *London Magazine*, *World Audience*, *Trespass*, and in monthlies like *She*. Her work has also been included in anthologies by Women Unlimited, Harper Collins, Oxford University Press, The New Oxford Writers and, most recently, in the award-winning collection by The Feminist Press of New York, *And the world changed – contemporary stories by Pakistani women*, where hers was the title story. A graduate of the University of Oxford's Master of Studies in Creative Writing programme, she is currently working on her first novel, *Once we were beautiful*.

**Emily Raboteau** is the author of the novel, *The professor's daughter*, and *Searching for Zion*, a work of creative non-fiction. The recipient of a Pushcart Prize and the *Chicago Tribune* Nelson Algren Award, Emily has received fellowships from the National Endowment for the Arts, the New York Foundation for the Arts, the Christopher Isherwood Foundation, and MacDowell. Her writing has been published in *Tin House*, the *Guardian*, the

*Huffington Post, Best American short stories, Best African American fiction* and *Best American non-required reading.* She lives in New York.

# 1 Fred D'Aguiar

*Grandfather calypso*

I hear him before I see him. He enters the front yard of his farm on his return from the rum shop. He never smokes, not even a clay pipe. He never chews tobacco. He keeps a pencil stashed behind his ear for easy reach – notes, reminding him to do something or other, on-the-spot sketches, of ideas for improving the farm. The calypso he intones topped the charts years ago. It's the one about the bucket with a hole. The owner of the bucket implores someone or other to check out the hole by sticking a proverbial finger into it. Of course there is no such bucket and the woman's licentious invite to her man, or a prospective man, raises a smile every time I hear it, especially from the lips of this old man, my grandfather. He roams bareheaded in the tropics known for baking scalps. Today, a Sunday afternoon, his pistol glaring in the belt, he finds it difficult to lift the rope hooked over the gate post, something he does not usually think about doing. His song fades as he struggles with pulling the rope off the post. He tries too hard and his hand flies up to his face. He shakes off the blow, curses as loud as his song, absentmindedly fingers his pistol and steps around the gate, careful, even in his inebriated condition, to return the hook over the post and secure the gate to prevent livestock wandering out. He aims for the red sand path that leads to the house and resumes singing.

'Oh Lawd, me bucket got a hole in de centre. And if you think I telling lie, push you finger.'

We conspire, together, that bucket and me, as it exhales Grandfather's ectoplasm from its dead black-hole centre. He unwittingly glides, legless, wide-eyed and airborne, from that enclosure. He exits along a blood path fringed with greenery. In his transformed state he holds the key to a gateway into his past that enables him to fly once more just for me; from Madeira on a Schiff loaded with silk and powered by silk sails, cargo he loses bolt by bolt as he trades his way from shore to shore to this song and dance routine of rum and recovery and flight and arrival. He leaves a flammable vapour trail. I see through it as I see through him, his outline the only definite thing. He cannot stop singing. If he stops I lose him as I almost do that moment he pauses his song to unhook the noose at the gate. He is here to shoot his wife, my grandmother, and I am the only other soul in the house, and so I become the last impediment between him and his goal.

He sings as if he is the one who wields the bucket of desire. He invites my curiosity; my finger. I sing along with him. But he must not reach the house. Or if he does, he must not lay eyes on my grandmother. Even though he walks at a rum pace, the path to the house stays exactly that distance of fifty yards from the front porch to the gate. Everything revolves, yet the gap between us remains the same. The whole scene looks curved; the gate, the path, the house and surrounding fields painted on a giant globe. At first he is just a song to me. No body. Not the man who I measured myself against with imaginary marks year after year, from thigh to waist, from navel to chest, as if he were a door post. My sight of him connects us. I fight to keep hold of this sight of him since he is a faint outline of a man whose surroundings outshine him. The relentless spit and polish of the sun on leaf, bark, grass, wire, stone. Whatever pours from the bucket that he sings about falls straight into my ears as if someone wants to fill a barrel using a useless container, one that leaks not water but a song, a song that won't be contained or channelled; one that spills.

He must not make it to the house. Grandfather starts his walk and resumes his song and both his steps and his singing stop abruptly as he keels over and clutches his chest. One moment he is singing and perambulating, the next he stops and folds his body, grabs his chest, appears to gasp and crumples to the ground. I hear him and see him fall. A gap opens between us. I hear the last few words after he utters them, as his body folds away into the ground. He finds an exit right there where he drops, an overripe fruit, his act of diminishing happens along with his song – I hear it and see him. Granddad! I run on the globe that spins with his walk but my run against the spin started by him leaves me trotting on the spot, unable to close the gap between us. That is where he leaves me as he exits this world for one entered through a song, through a bucket with a hole in the middle of it.

There is no following him, no catching up with him. No way of saying that his song is safe with me now that he abandons singing for silence. At some point the spin of the globe reverses in my favour. His steps no longer add to the momentum of the globe and my steps bring the globe to a stop and start it spinning towards me. The gap closes between us as I keep calling his name and run to meet him. His clothes, the colour of afternoon in the tropics, blend with the landscape. To see him I have to look hard at the ground where I believe he must be waiting for me. I cannot afford to blink. I run and stare and call his name and the ground revolves under my feet.

But he disappears into the red path where he fell. It absorbs him wholesale or he sinks into it wholesale. That is my wish for him – *Grandfather, disappear from my sight, save me from facing you.* That the earth would take him rather than have him take my grandmother from me, the sheer will of it on my part, causes him to fold away into earth before my eyes. At least for his walk up to the house my wish makes the earth concertina, compress all its thirty-two cardinal points to a globe as big as a house and front yard. My grandfather walks and spins the globe under his feet. I walk towards him or imagine I do and this movement of mine creates a counter-spin. As he falls, more a trip and doubling over, the globe slows, stops and reverses its spin. Slow at first then at a pace as fast as his walk towards me.

His song comes from belief that his wife offered her bucket to another man and that man, his drinking buddy who owns the village rum shop on land rented from Granddad, took up her invitation to push his proverbial finger into it. How Granddad decides about the meaning of the song happens by chance. The tune blares on the radio and my grandmother sings along with it, unaware that he stands just outside the door of the living room with a partial view of her singing and swaying to the music. I'm seated at the dining room table with my books spread out, some on the floor, people step around, doing my homework from table to floor and back, depending on the reference. The song ends and another less raucous and of no significance begins. I tune out the DJ saying the title and singer. Granddad disappears into the bedroom with a broom in his hand and Grandmother goes back to handling laundry.

I return my gaze to my geography textbook: a large, outsized affair with two facing pages of the same map of the world from two viewpoints – Mercator's and Peter's projections. The textbook invites the viewer to think about how politics influences geography. As a subject in a former colony I am supposed to abhor Mercator and adore Peter's correction of the proper landmass for Africa and South America. My grandmother's head whips around and turns in such a way – her chin over her right shoulder, her neck muscles stretched to capacity – that seeing her attention captured so completely makes me look as well. And there is Granddad vacating the front yard without a word to anyone, on a Sunday afternoon, with his pistol stuck in his belt, when a hat would have been more useful. She stares at him over her right shoulder and as he walks out of the yard she keeps up her action of hanging clothes on the line that runs from the upstairs balcony to a nearby sycamore tree, placing each item and pinning it with wood clothes pins by touch alone, as her head and her chin sustain an angle not possible for neck bones unless pressured abnormally, not by muscles, they are not sufficient, but by will.

The second that Grandfather unhooks the gate, steps around a narrow opening and hooks the gate shut again my grandmother abandons the bucket of clean clothes. She wipes her hands on her apron, unknots it from around her waist and lifts the apron over her head as she strides from the balcony into the house. Without a telephone in the house she needs some other means of communication with the outside world. She glances around her, claps eyes on me and calls me over, 'Come here, child', said in a way that compels me to leave my homework spread on the table and hurry to her.

'Go to the rum shop for me, cut across the field, run tell Mr Chapman your grandfather coming with a purpose. Quick, go.'

'Yes, Granny.'

The road to the rum shop curves away from the house and the bend, a double bend really, twisted one way then another in an S-turn before it opens up in a short straight with the rum shop on the left side of the road. Even with my speed across the field, past the pond, through a hole in the wood fence and behind a neighbour's house where family graves languish shadowed by a grove of coconut palms; even with my barefoot way of sprinting as if I have eyes in my feet, to avoid stones that grab nails off toes and splinters that burrow into a careless heel or sole, I know it will still leave me in the open, that I will have to cross the road to the rum-shop-side and anyone emerging from the S-curve and into the straight part of that road will see me.

But I have my marching orders from a woman known by everyone as 'she-who-will-be-obeyed', so despite the evidence of my rapid calculations, I take a deep breath and bound down the steps at the back of the house, skipping two and three at a time with a loose grip of the banister to prevent me tumbling head over heels. I leap the last three steps and land at the bottom of the stairs on both feet. A donkey brays from the direction of the road – long hee-haws that strike me as equivalent to the longest yawn of a night watchman near the end of his shift. I don't even look at the road as I run for the side of the house. But I can see that donkey, pointed ears and all of his frame garnered behind his braying. Maybe my grandfather pauses to look at the driver of the cart harnessed to the donkey. Or if like me he is intent of getting to his destination, he ignores driver and donkey for a more deserving target of his attention. Thinking of Grandfather making his way along the shorter route to the rum shop and of my need to reach him by taking the long way around distracts me enough to make me fail to slow down in time. I run slap-bang into the fence. I drop to half my five-feet-five, not dazed, or if I am, scratched and bruised with no time to pay attention. I scrunch myself to half my size in order to squeeze through that fence, first my head, followed by my shoulders, body aimed sideways-on. I do not breathe so much as exhale as I duck through the fence and exit my orderly yard for the uncultivated field. I run along the path that twists left and right across the field. My pace, just short of a sprint, turns out to be a little too fast for the sharp turns in the path. My feet clip the corners of the path and my arms whip against the longer, straggling stems of razor grass that creep imperceptibly in secret reclamation of the wild, a wild that we clear and clear again with instruments such as cutlasses and hoes and spades that act like toothpicks aimed at a shark's mouth. I fight back a sneeze induced by my leaving the cool of the house too fast for the oven of outdoors and by my drawing too hard on the baked air. A ram materialises in my path. Grazing. Head-down, tail-wriggle amble as if that four-legged creature owns the world. I charge at it and shout 'shoo' and wave my arms but it has no time to bolt out of my way and merely lifts its head up, chops full of a juicy clump of grass. At the last moment I leap as high as my legs will let me. The ram manages a half-turn to avoid me, just as I become airborne. I pull my legs up as hard and as fast as I can and almost close my eyes in anticipation of hitting the sheep and tumbling to the ground. I feel nothing, no crash of my feet against the close-cropped woollen back, no thump of my limbs against unaccommodating ground. I look, land, stumble one, two, three steps and windmill my arms to recover and keep running with a glance behind me in time to catch the ram's head-down sprint along the path in the opposite direction. He seems to butt my trailing shadow. His back legs shoot out and if my shadow happened to be me then I would have caught the mallets of his hooves squarely on my hindquarters. The close shave spurs me onwards, more adrenaline fires and adds juice to my legs and opens new pockets in my lungs.

The graveyard's concrete oblongs and crisscross grass paths resemble a chessboard. The two ways to get from one side to the other loom large: the first, along twisting paths, involves a slow pace and lots of adjustment in opposing directions, the second and more difficult way demands a higher degree of coordination and athleticism since it means hopping and leaping from grave to grave but in a time-saving straight line. The trouble with the second option harks back to tradition: children should never step on or over the graves of the dead but must respectfully walk around the graves, sticking to the grass paths. I take my orders from Grandmother as my permission to break this rule. If anyone, big or small, sees me and says anything, I'll just tell them that I am on an urgent mission for Grandmother and if they doubt me they should go to her and ask for themselves, but kindly step out of my way and stop delaying me with nonsense talk. Well, I would never add the latter part, that's too disrespectful, but as I labour to breathe my thinking process disposes with niceties.

I hop onto the first grave whose gray concrete signals its age. I should know who lies down there in that dark, but today I cannot remember and I resist the temptation to cast a quick eye over the headstone. I use my arms to help me add lift to my left-legged push off that gray concrete and I aim for the next grave. Here, the brighter concrete signals a more recent addition, but still years away from my memory of it. Already I look ahead to the next landing site. Already the next step and leap and the next draw my focus. This one stride over paths from grave to grave in a triple-jump sort of motion without the final jump, with a hop and step and hop again, now to smaller concrete, a child's size, not new, not someone I knew – I heard about him drowning in the pond that was filled in to honour his loss and the same grassy depression we ask the grownups to make into a pond again, but they offer the same excuse of his memory located right at that spot where he lost his life – and I cannot help myself but risk a glance at his stone and pick up his seven years of grace, which makes me almost lose my stride as I see his neat bones under my feet, small bones, clean now and I do not see the next grave, at least I fail to see until too late, that this next one has no concrete, is just a mound of dirt for the woman who never married into the family but bore two children and died with the third still in her and so her grave makes me stumble and put my hands down to save landing on my face and eating the dirt packed over her, but I cannot do more than pick myself up and think of Grandmother's urgent direction to me and I rush on with a step into the path before a leap onto the next grave and that way, one after another, the graves line up like stones over a river for me to take them one by one and cross that hallowed ground and I look ahead to just two more and want to glance back at how many I stepped on, how many helped me on my way, but the last two make me queue my legs and arms and hop and step and hop again and dream ahead to the path that leads to the rum shop where I will warn Mr Chapman that Grandfather coming with a pistol.

That last grave belongs to my father. The concrete on it looks bright, almost fresh, or so it feels to me when I see and feel it underfoot and can barely summon the energy to push from it. My body moves ahead of me onto the flat ground of the path. I watch myself do this look and leap thing. That is me. My arms pumping, my legs treating the air like a stepladder. The ball of my left foot sticks to my father's grave. I remain there, a stone statue of an athlete, with my head turned sideways to read the letters on the headstone. I stay there for the longest while in a time without end. For he appears at the front of the house in a car and in a wheelchair with an oxygen tank between his legs and a thin plastic tube from the tank to his nose. I rush to him and he is too weak to lift his arms off his lap and return my embrace. His smile barely rises around the corners of his mouth and not a trace of a shine in his eyes, green, but glazed, pupils dilated. I take over the job of pushing his chair, helped by a grownup. The red path on which we roll marbles and think so smooth, that leads from the road to the house, seems rutted for the wheels of my father's chair. The sand grips the wheels and threatens to gobble up the chair with my father in it. The grownup takes over but I keep one hand on the chair and walk along beside my father. I do not sleep that first night at the foot of his bed but listen for any movement from him and all I hear all night is him breathing, all shallow and quick with a whiff of panic around every draw and exhalation. And by the first cock's crow I wake with a start to a burst of prayer and crying and the grownups around him and he absent from himself.

His grave smells of concrete. I push away from his grip on my ankle. In one leap and a stride, I catch up with the part of me on a mission for my grandmother. My grandfather somewhere on the main road, the donkey and cart there as well, the bray of the donkey reclaimed by the infinite deep of blue sky, my father under my feet in every blade of grass, that ram eating bits of my father, so I fancy, and my father's return to airborne pollen, to dust picked up by a breeze and lifted into infinite sky and perhaps my father's face in one of those endless cloud formations drifting across the bigger visage of domed sky.

At this point, I guess, I must be adjacent to the two bends in the road. I need only run to a trench and jump it at its narrowest point, and turn towards the road. And in one final sprint to the side of the road, keep my stride, look left and right for traffic, with an extra glance in the direction where the road bends, before I scoot across to the rum shop. Assuming Granddad saunters as he habitually does, lifting his knees extra high and dropping the balls of his feet tentatively as if solid ground might at any moment become liquid, the man never to be hurried, he who all foot traffic overtakes, who shouts after me more than once his refrain sent to no one in particular, 'Hurry, hurry, make bad curry.' I afford that extra glance and expect to see just wavering heat that converts tarmacadam to sea ripples. I assume that even this Sunday afternoon robbed of its studied lackadaisicalness by him won't alter his pace. I think my urgency should beat that same meandering grandfather and I should reach Mr Chapman first and warn him about what my grandmother said and watch him take the right course of action. Which is what? What exactly does my grandmother's message mean to convey to Mr Chapman? Am I the bearer of doom for my grandfather in preference to a cheery rum-pushing neighbour? What if Mr Chapman thanks me for my message and then he reaches for his rifle that he keeps under the counter? I would be the one who warned him. My grandfather's grave next to my father's would surely stop me from ever entering that field again and stop me seeing anything but my place among them, since the rest of my days and nights would consist of me trapped in re-runs bearing Grandmother's message that resulted in my grandfather's death.

I slow down, labour to breathe. I could keep up my sprint breathing like this but the thought of bringing something unforeseen onto Granddad's head slows me down. The trench widens and narrows as it toggles from the road, cuts through the field and enters as a dark scar into the coconut groves. I head for a narrow section trying my best to keep up a forward trajectory. The grass thickens near the water. A few sheep graze nearby and do not bother to look up to see me. I ignore them in my keenness to find a dry spot to leap across the trench. I spot what appears to be a log, wet in parts and muddy as the trunk of a tree. The log, draped over the trench, forms an almost straight line, a log with a twist to it, but conveniently positioned from one side of the trench to the other. I choose it as my crossing point. I aim for the log and pick up speed, determined to step on it and propel myself to the other side of the trench without so much as a squidgy of mud on my heels. To treat it like another grave underfoot. Here we go, I tell myself. I picture how my take-off and landing goes before I start either. I take a deep breath and hold it in for the full benefit and launch myself at the log. I'm already ahead of myself, halfway up the bank of the trench before I take that first step on the log. My left leg leads and it hits the log with all my weight pivoted on that foot. A message races up my heel, along my backbone and sparks in my skull with sufficient charge to it to make me adjust my eyes from the other side of the bank to the spot immediately under my foot.

I look but do not register what I see. After all, I am on a mission. I carry an urgent message from my grandmother for Mr Chapman. Remember your grandfather. I tell myself this, not so much in words but in a flash of recognition. My grandfather left the house with his pistol tucked in his belt and without a hat on his head in the tropics that bakes grass even as the grass stands valiantly against it and entire battalions wither, fold over and turn brown. I cannot pause to look at peculiarities in nature, not now. Other days I wandered here and there doing just this, looking to see what nature has in store for me and finding the odd wild berry to chump on along the way and chewing non-stop on a teeth-cleaning stick. Not today. Not now. No time for close-ups. But the note to my head fires several times in that millisecond, so much so that I cannot ignore it. The note sent up my nerves is about texture, that the bark under my foot is hard but with a peculiar softness to it, that the log adjusted itself under my weight though surprisingly not just where my foot landed, in obedience to the laws of physics, but along its entire length, that the log sprouts a head, legs and a tail, and both head and tail twist in contrapuntal rhythm, and lastly, but not good for my breathing which switches from deep and therapeutic to shallow and stuttered, at the far end of the log a split opens and jagged teeth show. Before I think the word 'alligator' I shoot bodily from that log, some trigger mechanism in my left leg's calf and thigh fires me vertically and I bicycle in the air, I windmill my arms, and succeed in travelling horizontally for several feet. The acre of grass, graves, trees that surrounds me shrinks and expands, banishing everything except that log come alive as alligator; that log and me riding above it without benefit of a saddle and bridle.

How can the air present a ladder to me, one that I climb up and clamber down? It's the air that I don't breathe. Unused by me and perhaps grateful to me for not using it up, it forms a ladder for me. I leap from the back of the alligator and climb in a cycle action up the rungs on that ladder made of air and avoid the snap of the alligator's elevated jaws. I land on the other side of the trench, just out of reach of the alligator which moves along the trench in anticipation that since I went up I must surely come down somewhere nearby. I look over my shoulder with a stretched twist of my neck very much like my grandmother's neck-stretch-twist when she latched onto my grandfather as he departed the house with his pistol on his waist. The few sheep nearby dart from the alligator in three directions, all bays and kicks and mad swirls of their tails. The slope up the trench yields to my feet without my attention. I shake my head and feel my chest burn and heave. I almost come to a standstill to nurse a stitch in my side. Instead, I press on my stomach with my left hand and stumble onto the side of the road.

I look in the direction of the bend and dearly want Granddad there at the mouth of it, him seeing me and shouting ahead to me that my hurry, hurry, antics would surely result in a bad curry. The sight of him would be enough to stop me in my tracks and force me to wait for him to catch up with me and make me fail on my mission. I think his figure wavers in that heat, evolves tremblingly out of it, boneless and elastic at first, before it forms the solid thing of him.

'Hurry, hurry, make bad curry!'

'Granddad?'

'Over here, fool.'

I whip my head around from the road in the direction of the house and towards where his voice comes from and there he is framed, like a gunslinger in the Wild West, if only he had on a hat, in the front door of Mr Chapman's rum shop.

'What brings you here in such a hurry, son?'

'I running to avoid the sun, Granddad.'

'You have a message for me?'

'Yes, Granddad.'

And here I inhale deeply, twice, to buy time and conjure up something convincing. What I come up with sounds lame to my ear but it is all I can muster at short notice.

'Granny said not to drink too much because you and she have a church function this evening.'

'Okay, you must have wings on your feet. Come in for a soft drink.'

I walk up to him and he ruffles my head. We turn and walk into the cool and fermented sugar smell. A handful of tables, scattered haphazard like dice on the worn wood floor, stop their dominoes chatter. All eyes dart from

Granddad to Mr Chapman and back to Granddad, more his waistline than his face but certainly not at me. I catch a variety of nods and touching of hats as the men greet my grandfather – Mr D'Aguiar, the name taken up by each table like an orchestra warming up for a conductor. They finish their drinks in single gestures of heads thrown back, chairs scrape on the wood floor and the men beeline for the door and just like that the place is left to Granddad, Mr Chapman and me. Mr Chapman flashes a smile and shouts at me from his station behind the counter.

'What you drinking, boy?'

I look up at Granddad and he nods and smiles down at me and I beam back at him.

'A ginger beer, please, Mr Chapman.'

I summon all my will to stop my eyes drifting from Granddad's sun-beaten face down to his waist. We head for the nearest table and sit. I twirl a round beer mat on the zinc table.

'How come you reach here so fast, Granddad?'

'Just as I walk out the gate I meet our neighbour and his donkey and cart full of empty barrels heading for the standpipe, so I hop on and fly here.'

I nod and smile and wipe my forehead with my bare forearm. Granddad takes his handkerchief from his back pocket and he leans towards me and he wipes my face with three deft strokes – one on my left temple and jawbone, one across my forehead, and the third along my right temple and jaw all the way across my chin, which he mock punches with the handkerchief balled in his fist.

'Thanks, Granddad.'

'Boy, you look just like your father and you always in a hurry just like he used to be.'

He wipes his neck and folds his kerchief deliberately and tucks it into his trouser pocket by easing his weight a little off the chair. I want to hear more about my father. But Granddad looks over at the bar at Mr Chapman. I gulp my ginger beer.

'Easy now my little steam train, you don't want to give yourself cramps by throwing a lot of cold stuff into the furnace.'

Mr Chapman laughs as he says this and Granddad joins in with him. Without changing his position of facing us from behind the bar, Mr Chapman reaches around to his right side and plucks a bottle off the counter. He fishes two glasses from rows stacked face down to his left, both glasses in his left hand, and deposits them neatly, face up on the bar. He pours from the bottle into both glasses, moving the bottle-mouth from the lip of one glass to the other without upending it. Granddad nods at him approvingly and Mr Chapman leaves his place behind the bar with the two glasses in his hand. He pulls a chair over to our table and holds out his arm with the two glasses in it and Granddad takes one glass and they clink, raise their glasses and tilt their chins. Both men smack their lips and exhale loudly as the red rum catches fire in their mouths, throats and stomachs. I sip my ginger beer, eyeing each man in turn. No one speaks for a few moments. I see my ginger beer bottle sweat condensation. A bead materialises at the neck and runs higgledy-piggledy down the side gathering volume and speed until it reaches the base of the bottle and splits in two directions to form the beginnings of a ring around the base.

I drain my bottle and realise, just as I spy through the bottom of the bottle the long fluorescent tube hanging on two cobwebbed chains in the centre of the room, that I should have taken longer to drink the treat. Neither man offers me another and I start to summon up the courage to ask for more, but know that any such move on my part would be extremely rude in the face of the generosity I already enjoyed.

'Okay, son, you should get back now. Tell your grandmother I'll see her in a while.'

I get this pit and hollow feeling in my stomach as though my guts and ribs gone from there and leave this space for dread to take root and prosper. I want to grab Granddad's hand and lead him from the company of Mr Chapman. I even see myself doing just that and in my desolation I push my chair away from the table and let the legs scrape on the floor against all my better training to always leave a table by lifting the chair from under me.

Granddad grabs his pencil from behind his ear and scribbles something on a beer-stained placemat which he presses into my hand but takes a moment to keep his grip on me and look me in the eye.

'Give this to your grandmother.'

'Yes, Granddad.'

'Now go, as fast as you came.'

'Yes, Sir. Bye, Mr Chapman.'

At the rum shop door, I steal a glance back at the two men. Granddad replaces the pencil behind his left ear and raises his glass towards Mr Chapman's. I do not hear the actual clink as their glasses collide but I summon it from their previous toast and paste it to this second good-health wish. I walk out into the sunlight, a hot vice which clamps onto my head and neck. Where should I go with Granddad's message but back to the house? And fast, to report to Grandmother that I could say nothing to Mr Chapman and hope she has a plan B.

Run as I should, I cannot. My legs feel leaden. They feel filled with cold. I picture them as two bottles filled with immobilising ginger beer and this image saves me from thinking of the worst. I force myself to trot across the road saying aloud to myself that it is safe to spend as little time as possible in a space designed for speed. The smooth tarmac, that so many cars underestimate and careen into each other at one turn or other of that S-bend, keeps its liquid glare, the ripples of an old carpet, the smell of a cauldron of tar and stone. I decide to take the road home at a trot-pace. The trench looks innocent from the road, a fixed geography of inviting twists and turns so unlike the brute life I brushed up against when I crossed there. For an instant, I convert the entire length of the trench, from the road to the coconut groves, into one giant, hugger-mugger caiman, an invitation to an unwary flock, or child. And just then I arm myself with a lasso, no saddle, and a cowboy hat stringed in place under my chin; I become a giant of a man and I ride that trench-turned-caiman with spurs sprouted from my heels, gallop with it away from these fields down to the sea and across the sea to join my absent mother and brothers. A car horn blares as the car blasts past me, followed really closely by another and another – a three-car race that may end badly at some other turn farther up the road. I wave without looking to see who it might be and a part of me wishes to be next to one driver or other looking at the blur of this countryside sliding off the windscreen with insect houses and insect pedestrians. This is me trying to keep Granddad's scribbled message to my grandmother out of my mind, fighting the impulse to look at it by applying my mind wholesale to every other possibility. I am so engrossed in this mental gymnastics of fabrication taken up by my imagination to hold at bay some more terrible reality that I miss entirely the arrival at my heels of the braying donkey and cart. I bolt around to face water barrels spilling their precious cargo as the barrels rock to the donkey's trot. The spillages too fast to follow land on the road and pop up as dark bruises, black marks which immediately turn to nuggets of steam and disappear. The driver hails me and I recognise the farming neighbour, a new tenant on Granddad's farm. He stops for me and I look up and down the road before hopping up beside him. He clicks his tongue and flicks the reins, not a real flick, just an automatic notice to the donkey to resume its trot. The donkey stays on the spot until the last ounce of air runs out and stifles its braying, puts its head down and jerks the cart forward from a crawl to a walk to a gentle trot as nimble as the waves rising off the road.

'First your grandfather, now you; I should start charging.'

'Yes, Sir, you would become rich.'

'I hear you good at school.'

'Thank you, Sir.'

'Keep up those books and you going far.'

'I will, Sir.'

'You going to the church later?'

'Yes, Sir, everybody who is anybody got to be there. Not every day Deputy Minister come to our town.'

'You got that right. I hurrying to finish my chores early.'

'Me too.'

'Your granddad coming as well?'

'Yes, Sir, he not drinking much, just got some business with Mr Chapman.'

'On a Sunday? Must be important.'

'I don't know my grandfather's business. Could be rent.'

'Yep, not much round here that not on your granddad land.'

There is a lull in our talk and a slumber instilled by the rhythmic canter of the donkey and the Sunday-afternoon heat. The water drums rub against one another and even their metal-rubbed-on-metal sounds add to the lull. We leave prints on the tarmac, more little spills from the barrels. The spills dry up and disappear faster than a jet's vapour trail. One day that will be me up there winging my way to my mother and brothers. My mother is bound to send for me soon just as she sent for my three brothers, from the youngest up.

'Sir, what you call this donkey?'

'Hee-Haw. If you find something better in your books let me know.'

'That's a good name, Sir.'

'Whoa,' he says and pulls on the reins and Hee-Haw obeys in no time. I hop off and salute him and run to the gate, unhook the noose from the post, slide sideways in the small gap keeping a hand on the gate that would otherwise swing wide and push it back in line with the post as I replace the hooked rope. Hee-Haw starts to bray – a heave of air and wheeze of his innards and a launch of his crescendo. I turn from the gate and sprint along the cricket-pitch-smooth, red sand path to the house, looking for my grandmother and finding her right there on the front steps, not quite framed by the front door. I run to her and pull the beer mat from my pocket, and hand it to her with outstretched arm as if I'm in a relay.

'Don't worry, Grandson.'

She says this to me even before she reads his note. In fact, she turns her entire attention to me ignoring the beer mat in her right hand. She lays her left arm on my shoulder and steers me towards her body so that even as I try to move away from her to put some kind of shamefaced distance between us, her strong arm won't let me. She manoeuvres me into her body and I collide with her and she holds me there, pins me to her with her left arm. And right then and there my head turns dark. All the lamps in my head snuff their wicks all at once and the brightness in me dissolves to these pinpoints and I bury my face into her frock and cry, a hoarse, airless, donkey wheeze of an outburst as I struggle to catch my breath.

'I know you try your best. I see your grandfather climb on the cart and I call you back, but the donkey bray and deafen the place and drown out my voice.'

She moves a little from side to side, automatic for her, but her swaying takes me back too far. I see days with me in her lap and she in her rocking chair to cure me of some ailment or other and her talk under her breath that I can barely make out, that I try to listen to, that makes me doze off and forget the world. That child is not me. Not anymore. I feel embarrassed that she starts to move with me pinned to her as if that child could ever be me again. I switch off my voice and dry my eyes on my forearm. I think, 'push her away'. She reads my mind and unclasps her left arm.

'Read this to me. I don't have my spectacles.'

She holds up the beer mat. I squint at the pattern of beer stains superimposed on the advertisement of a bottle of the country's best hops bottled by the people for the people, a taste of things to come, the government motto says, for a new nation about to bring to reality some big dream about itself. Across the stains and motto and picture in bright blue ink I make out Granddad's flowery cursives – the ends of letters at the ends of words climbing in neat curves.

'Is it in Portuguese?'

'No, Grandmother.'

How do I tell her what I see? Just tell her. Her body absorbs grief like no other. I put it down to her demeanour, the sway of her floor-length dress, her speech that never admonishes, her feather-pillow-soft embrace, her as stoic witness to a burgeoning family graveyard. There is nothing she cannot withstand. She put her son, my father, into the ground. When Granddad fails to lift the first shovelful of dirt and sinks to one knee and hides his face in his forearm, she steps forward and takes the tool from him and with one arm pitches the shining muzzle into the mound of fresh soil and waves the shovel, as if sowing a field, over the hollow rectangle, only then uncles weigh in and aunts gather children into an arsenal of grief, including me, watching Grandmother's example, to keep my head clear, as my father would wish it. Someone offers a shovel to me. I shake my head and turn away and my grandmother pulls me into the arms where I remain to this day. I feel her body shudder though she makes no sound and her face streams. She sways and I listen for anything she might say. She drinks air, deep gulps and shallow sips, slow, fast, slow.

'Read the thing!'

'Yes, Grandmother.'

I breathe deep, lift my chin towards her ear and she inclines her head to me. I read in a secret whisper, a slow pour from my mouth into her ears. This is me with no trace of a sting in my voice that might hurt my grandmother, rounding off the hard edges of my grandfather's words seeing them as given to me, my body first, before I deliver them to my grandmother's.

*Dear bucket, I love you, too much to share you with another finger.*

There is no moisture in this heat. Sound travels in it, buoyed by it. A crow circling two hundred feet up clears its throat and I look up thinking that bird might be in the tree shadowing me, so it fetches to me all that way, in thin air, that clear. Same way I hear the donkey braying all day from any point in any field. Air shrinking distance. Air magnifying sound. That's how I hear one gunshot, and a second, folded into the echo of the first. My grandmother glances, the same time as me, towards the rum shop, and she covers her mouth and we retreat into the house and close the front door and wait for Grandfather to come home.

I follow her to the dining room, away from the windows facing the road. She takes the Bible and props the spectacles on her bulbous nose.

'You can look for him. Or you can help your cousins catch that alligator.'

I head for the front windows and lean out and squint at the road. The same heat and haze works against my determined eyes. Things unscramble for me, pull apart, and in their separation, solidify. With each step a figure advances from a portal of this heat and haze, where that figure languishes momentarily, delivered to that spot at that point in time as a loose bundle of particles. The act of placing one foot before the other appears to stitch all the parts of a body together from see-through to translucent to perspicacious as the hull of a ship so that the figure is whole, and there he is, Grandfather, wavering into view, his outline trembling in the heat.

As if heat can be a sound, a trumpet blares, a loudspeaker garbled at first and with feedback almost musical. The noise comes from the opposite direction to Granddad. A pick-up truck with loudspeakers mounted on top crawls along the liquid road and broadcasts a string of words swimming in a sea of echoes. *Come-com-com out-ut-ut and-nd-nd greet-eet-eet your-ur-ur deputy-pu-ty-ty information-ma-shon-shon minister-is-ter-ter at-at the-the Free-ee-ee Church-urch-urch at-at six-ix o-o'clock-ock-ock.* Over and over the message blares as the truck passes the house, beeps its horn twice and people on the truck wave at me, and I wave back. Others walk out of the shadows of houses and march up to the roadside to stand with hands shading eyes and stare and chat with each other. The truck moves along and the clusters break and retreat back into shadows. The vehicle draws level with Granddad and the announcement stops. Granddad explains something to the men. They nod and look at the house. He moves away and a watery gap opens between the van and Granddad. The loudspeaker resumes, a little quieter, now that it has passed the house and is indistinct once more, a sea of echoes.

# Reading myself as a stranger

There is a famous story about Wilson Harris (born 1921), the writer from Guyana. Apparently, he left Georgetown (the capital) to act as government surveyor of rivers in the rainforest interior. But when he got there and made his measurements of the rivers (principally, the Essequibo and its many tributaries) the readings were so illogical and differed so dramatically he doubted the veracity of his instruments. As a result he returned to the ordered grid system of the streets of the capital with his faith in writing revolutionised. He moved away from linear realism and opted for a more poetic, surreal portrayal of people and events. He invested more in the image as a reliquary of a character's motives and thinking and less in plot as a harbinger of intent. Having grown up in Guyana (I was born in London but spent my childhood in Guyana and returned to London as a teenager) I thought his way was as good a way as any to guide me into my fiction.

I start with an image of a person or a thing or a person attached to a thing, in this case an old man with a pistol out in the heat of a tropical afternoon without his hat. The image works in tandem with a mood, flavour and sound. If there is a colour for the scene it is red tinged and crowned with a blue haze. The sound of a donkey braying for a long time slows down the way the scene unfolds. The mechanical hands of a clock disappear and a relaxed pulse replaces the beat of the second hand. If there is a smell to this scene then it is of damp vegetation held under a hot lamp. I attach all this to a defining piece of language. In this case a line or two from a famous calypso. I want to see how much a line defines a life or how one or two lives may be attuned to a song. That song defines the lives to a large extent.

I try to define a traumatic moment by bringing a flux of actions to a standstill. I hold that moment and sketch it for the reader as an emotional construct, a set of feelings derived from the grandfather and grandmother, and the song. I want the feel for the story to flourish by an act of holding the danger high in the air in a freeze frame for the reader's prolonged scrutiny. I hope the reader feels the tension of what is about to unfold and delves into the character involved, their motives and memories and impulses.

Place plays a big part in all this. Place is a character as well. The place is alive and it affects the people in it. The tropical location happens to resemble Guyana, on South America's north coast, where I spent ten years as a child. The grandfather figure bears more than a passing resemblance to my grandfather, whose roots in Madeira and whose farming practices mirror that of the story's lead. But the actual event is made up. The use of my real surname and the real place gives the story its sense of a transmutation of autobiography into art. But it is autobiography doctored for narrative success. I invent and abandon loyalty to the facts as soon as I feel the need to increase that authentic feel of a story being told rather than a life narrated. The difference resides in the belief that fiction shapes autobiography as much as autobiography defines fiction. The writer embarks on an exploration of layered, wedding-tiered selves through the device of storytelling. And in complementary fashion, the story explores the writer as it unfolds. The writer discovers things as s/he looks into things.

It is not easy to say what a story means other than that there is a need to talk about the effect of reading or hearing a story. One major effect is emotional. The feelings engendered by reading a story, results in some intelligence about it. Certain things may be surmised by emotion and this means it is safe to credit emotion with intelligence. An emotional intelligence is at work because an intuitive intelligence helped to shape the story steeped in emotion. The collusion between what is felt and what is thought, these twin engines, power the sense of the story as an irresistible entity, as a world that cannot be ignored because it benefits the reader to know about it.

The chase in the story of the boy trying to out-run his grandfather and reach the rum shop ahead of his grandfather so that he can deliver his grandmother's message to the man who runs the rum shop appears iconic to stories invested in the chase. But it is more than the thrill of the ride. The journey across the field and graveyard and trench enables all manner of histories and geographies and psychological states to be entertained. Much of the traditional back story flourishes during the chase as incident and recall informing present action and feeling. The straight-line walk of the grandfather competes with the long loop run of the boy. Both inform the story but one, the loop, involves much more investigation and revelation than the linear narrative allows. It is a small argument to say that the story's narrative complexity should match the character's emotional complexity. But it is one worth making for a particular species of fiction invested in mirroring the complexity of consciousness and feeling.

I shy away from the thrill of the chase for the simple reason that it leads to a chase after more thrills. I prefer to explore the motives behind a character's impulse to sow chaos in a story. That impulse to satisfy a reader's need for a thrill appears to work in tandem with an absence of analysis of a character's motives for indulging in a concatenation of destructive actions. I introduce the idea of the thrill but choose instead to focus on the many impulses driving that action. While the reader is smart enough to supply the details of the drama that is suggested in the story, it would be presumptuous of me to expect the reader to infer from those actions the kind of emotional complexity that proves difficult to articulate and make real.

This is because emotions and their accompanying intuitive intelligence cannot be assumed as given in any scene or run of events. The scene may be loaded with feeling and implied thinking but the writer needs to draw on additional material to articulate the more remote and complicated aspects to any emotion or motive. It is this investigation that interests me and calls for a unique species of fictional depiction. And here I return to the idea of a stretched out or elongated moment in a narrative when the action is slowed or becomes a series of stills in order to tease out the feeling and thinking layered under and around it. The technique is not so much narrative as lyric. It borrows heavily from the procedure of the lyric poem where a moment in time or an event comes under scrutiny in a circular and lateral investigation of it. There is a deepening exploration rather than a narrative progression.

This anti-narrative narration, this lyric time rather than linear time progression, teases out the complex emotion and thinking behind a character's action and enables these revelations to percolate and surface in a reader's mind and heart. There is something akin to imagism in this idea, of an image that carries emotion and thinking, both of which survive as submerged realities in the picture. A good reader finds the buried entities by contemplating the picture. A good writer should trust in the veracity of the image to carry the argument. But the delayed fictional moment wishes to make additional commentary about how fiction works as a cognitive device. The lyric time (rather than linear) of the anti-narrative invites the reader to think about form and content as coterminous: how the story works becomes as important as what work the story does.

Theory about fiction runs the risk of trying to paraphrase the obvious. Fiction appears to carry its own reasons for being in the world. A story shows the world to the reader and tells the reader a little about itself. The way a story unfolds declares something about its process of making meaning. To a large extent a story's content and a story's form share the same territory. When form and content work together the two are bound inextricably. Ideally, the life of the story should not be seen as 'out there' or artificial but real somehow because experienced as emotion by the reader. Theories about how a story works and ways for reading it may be a function of reading experience. In other words the story instructs the reader how it should be read and, gradually, imperceptibly, educates that reader into the world of the story. This makes an author's essay about his story uncomfortably akin to an editor's return to the cutting room floor to see what might be rescued from it.

Alternatively, there is a belief that unless theory is a part of the conversation theory will go unheralded and there will remain in the narrative an absence of deliberation. This absence is a function of the fiction, brought out by the very existence of the story as a necessary corollary to it. However much theory may be viewed as lesser than the original theory reasons itself into being on account of the very existence of the story. It is as if the story is not quite complete without a discussion about it. This may be in recognition of the reader writer duality that surrounds the story: that after the story is written it needs to be read to complete its cycle of being. In the same way, in addition to being read, the story may need to be discussed, talked about so that Oscar Wilde's social dictum – that there is only one thing worse than being talked about, not being talked about – may apply to the story as well as it moves from the private sphere of the writer's world into the public domain of a gaining a readership.

To this end I offer my explanation and defence: that the true setting of this story should in no way undermine the high degree of fabrication involved in making it work as fiction; that the people in the story bear very little relation to the folk I knew in that familiar place. Though there was an alligator found draped across a trench and the coconut grove exists with its sprinkle of modest graves. The first-person narrator in the story is not me. I never came near to walking on the back of an alligator while I lived on my grandfather's farm forty miles from Guyana's capital – though I often dreamed that if I did, I would behave in exactly the terms ascribed to my main narrator of this story.

As for endings, the short story presents both open and closed possibilities, both the chance to tie up the parcel of loose ends in an artistic display of braggadocio and the more open-ended declaration of the impossibility of closure and of mimicking the untidiness of real life. The fact that both possibilities exist in a story suggests fiction's

31

grasp of contradiction as part and parcel of fiction's style and meaning. The abrupt ends of short stories point to a world that is largely suggested rather than ever fully constructed. Both open and closed endings invite a reader to do the work demanded by endings: that is, continue the involuntary act of writing as a reader after the story concludes. The life of the story continues in the mind of the reader. Ultimately, the line between real and imagined, between writer and reader, becomes blurred. One person delineates the process of creative thought on behalf of a created community so that reading by that community is tantamount to recognition of itself and sometimes, healthy surprise at how it is seen and depicted, surprise about some of the choices made by the writer.

Politics surfaces the moment the writer acknowledges a reading community. I do not mean the simplified duality of left and right, centre and periphery that typifies political parties. For writers the politics concerns certain ethical choices. If a situation appears unfair, if an underdog remains undefended, the writer wakes up to the call to represent that lack. How that manifests in a story depends on the writer, but for me it means that I focus on people and places and dilemmas underrepresented in the arts of the imagination. I really want my work to help make the world a better place for all. I see gestures of sticking the index finger into an open mouth but I stick to my claim: stories can and do heighten awareness of shortcomings in society and help to raise the ethical fibre of a community.

The writer does not have to encounter an overt instruction from landscape in order to try ways of writing that contravene linear and plot-driven stories. Wilson Harris was lucky to find his technique for prose in his life experience. Most others work it out by trial and error with sentences measured by what they imagine. The exact process of how aesthetics help in the formation of ethics remains part mystery, part alchemy, but the fact is that once exposed to stories people become sensitised to the world of that story in immeasurable ways. Enjoy.

# 2　Jane Draycott

*De Somniis*

So there at the top, one foot already descending,
you hesitate, beautiful object in your pyjamas –
*bad luck to cross on the stairs,* which leaves me wondering
what goods or gifts we might have traded if we'd met:
not just the beaten gold-work, silk and spices
from another age and climate, but perhaps
some *lingua franca* we'd devise by night
up on the ribboning road, or best, some manuscript
in your own hand, a chromosome or two, a hand
before we passed from out each other's sight,
so this was not the end of days and us
two continents apart, but more like something
sent by a deity, a dream of the first class.

## *Why some people like to keep chickens*

Returned one day from who knows where
you'll climb the stairs, each step a flight
into the roof-space as it might appear

where there's a room which like a lover waits –
some books, a sofa and the perfect light,
a quiet carpet like a grassy hill

although in truth the books seem flat and dull
and written in a tongue you cannot understand
so all that's left to do is lie out on the ground

and gazing through the leaves and branches listen
to all the intelligent tackle of the world,
its noise and hardware coming across the sidings

and audible there above the rosary
of transatlantic flights, the sound of chickens
and the geese she will be keeping, and of her crying

all that night and day again whenever it will be.

# The staircase

There's a staircase that appears in your recurring dreams, and a room at the top which you can't quite see. Forget it if you can. Jung and Freud have told you what a staircase might represent or symbolise. Forget that too if possible. I recognise it now, it's the staircase in the flat where I lived as a nineteen-year-old student, my first independent life away from home. We were on the ground floor, and in all the years I lived in that house I never went up those stairs.

Who knows where the ideas in poems come from? Edwin Morgan counselled poets strongly against self-consciousness: 'I cannot imagine anything more likely to inhibit them from writing...' (*The poet's voice and craft*, p. 54). Certainly those ideas are easier to think about after a poem is written than before, when to talk about them is generally to talk a poem out of existence. The great French photo-journalist Henri Cartier-Bresson maintained that it was the photograph that took him – 'C'est la photo qui nous prend'(*Photo* no. 144). For some reason, the image of a staircase has twice taken my imagination recently, in two different poems written six months apart. I was unaware of the connection between them, though I can see now that the staircase in both is a hallucinatory version of that same real staircase in East Finchley. The poetic imagination, however, isn't interested so much in what things are really like as in what they suggest. Which is why, having recognised that quiet detonation with which a new poem flicks into life, I knew on both occasions that there was a way to go till I could start – I had to wait.

'De Somniis' started life as I paused one day at the top of a staircase at work to let someone come up before I went down. I knew there was something in the moment that wanted following after like a tracker dog or divining rod till it found its material: *its road, its tale, its desire* as Don Paterson has so memorably expressed it (*Aphorisms*, p. 285). The superstition about crossing on the stairs was only a first thought, a 2-D poem at most. The association with the dream of Jacob, the heavenly ladder, angels ascending and descending, came soon enough but it was an over-familiar trope. The poem had to move forward and elsewhere from there and I had to wait for the rest to present itself in the way Robert Frost has described the poet's process, 'kicking ourselves from one chance suggestion to another in all directions as of a hot afternoon in the life of a grasshopper' (Frost, *Complete poems*).

This scanning, waiting for the additional layers of imagery and narrative to stick 'like burrs' as Frost puts it, seems important. It's a part of the process by which the material from one's everyday apprehension of the world draws on and is ignited by ideas or images beyond it, and vice versa. A subject won't give itself up to you stared at straight on. Like the faint constellation of the Pleiades, it is seen more brightly by looking slightly to one side. About a week after the incident on the stairs I caught the end of a radio interview about the 'horizontal' historical line created by long-standing trade routes. I had no notion where these disconnected ideas might lead if put together but by now I had an invented first scene in my head and I began the first draft almost in the spirit of a fiction writer – as Neil Gaiman has said of writing *American gods*, 'I wrote it to find out what happened next' (*Guardian*, 'On writing American gods').

The initial ideas for 'Why some people like to keep chickens' arrived in the reverse order, sparked by a radio report on how in times of crisis growing numbers of people in the West are taking up back-yard pastoral pleasures such as keeping chickens or bees. Just an account of the phenomenon wasn't a poem in itself. Another 2-D notion so far. When I waited to see what other ideas might gather like dust on the static of the first, the image of a staircase presented itself. It took the poem to work out why – I went up the stairs as I had in my dream, having no real idea where it might lead.

This associative method of composition, slow as it may seem, strikes me as an active reflection of how we operate in the everyday non-literary world, making associations, building meaning and narrative from connections and patterning. It is not that one wants to by-pass conscious ideas when approaching a poem, nor undervalue the power of narrative. Far from it. But just as in our non-writing life we never truly know what is going to happen next, what I was looking for each time was the poem beyond the poem I sat down at first to write. All the interest, the pleasure, the discovery comes when you push at the additional doors in a first idea. Why stop in the hallway when the house, like a vast advent calendar, offers so many other openings?

*Imagined not recalled*
So the process of feeling in the dark for a poem begins. Rather than drop the biblical association in 'De Somniis', I followed a trail from it to the early history of dream-theory. Here seemed something hopeful in the medieval interest in the ideal, the best we could achieve, which connected somehow – though I didn't know how in narrative or structural terms – with the historical development of the trade routes and the staircase image. The 'you' swiftly became an invented, inverted *you* set free from the

'truth' of the poem's occasion, a conflation of all kinds of people I've seen coming down towards me from the tops of different staircases at different points in my life. An invention, a dramatisation, but made out of experienced and remembered real moments which are the deep battery power for the piece, abstracted far enough to set off what turns out to be almost a love poem. An alloy of both the imagined and recalled, as Lowell's opposition in his poem 'Epilogue' has it (Lowell, *Day by day*, p. 127).

The *you* of the elegiac 'Why some people like to keep chickens' is a less dramatised figure, though still aiming towards John Keats' talismanic definition of a poet as being 'the most unpoetical of any thing in existence; because he is continually infor[ming] – and filling some other body' (Gittings (ed.) *Letters of John Keats*, p. 157). Using the simultaneous projection-and-viewing lens of the second person address, the apprehension in the poem has it both ways, at once objective and subjective. It's a device very movingly used in Michael Donaghy's late poem 'Exile's end', also elegiac in tone:

> You will do the very last thing...
> Observe the skilled frenzy of the physicians,
> a nurse's bald patch, blood. These will blur,
> as sure as you've forgotten the voices
> of your childhood friends, or your toys.
> Or, you may note with mild surprise,
> your name...
>
> (*Safest*, p.46)

The best poems are complex in their layering, delivering a strong associative charge in addition to their surface narratives, and a great deal of that associative life is of course generated by metaphor – the striking together of two ideas

40

or scenarios which fire simultaneously like superimposed films. Take for example Keith Douglas' image of the night sky as a battlefield in his early poem 'Stars', written in 1940 as he waited to go to the front:

The stars still marching in extended order
Move out of nowhere into nowhere. Look, they are halted
On a vast field tonight...

*(The complete poems,* p. 29)

So one proceeds with the door open onto the dream-like world of the subconscious, experimenting with the fusion of several strands of imagery and narrative. A poem at this point is almost beyond you. You are playing it like an instrument, with your breath and the pressure of your fingers, trying to give it voice and shape until one day the poem turns towards its close, in a process not unlike that described in John McGahern's great novel *That they may face the rising sun*: 'You never know rightly what you are facing into when you're setting out. You always know the way home'(*Rising sun*, p. 150).

Of the two poems, 'Why some people keep chickens' has the more straightforward movement, taken directly from my actual dream. Remembered dreams don't usually make good poems, they are too complete. But I was caught by the structure offered by the dynamic arc of the flight of stairs, the lifting trajectory leading upwards and elsewhere. It's a trajectory at the heart of the subtle slow ascent in the structure of Joyce's story *The dead*, which opens as Gabriel arrives 'scraping his feet vigorously while the three women went upstairs... . He looked up at the pantry ceiling, which was shaking with the stamping and shuffling of feet on the floor above,' and closes with the visionary view from a high window: 'It had begun to snow again... It was falling on every part of the dark central plain, on the treeless hills, falling softly upon the Bog of Allen and, farther westward, softly falling into the dark mutinous Shannon waves ... His soul swooned slowly as he heard the snow falling faintly through the universe' (*Dubliners*, pp. 139–40).

Wallace Stevens famously noted that 'All poetry is experimental poetry' (*Opus posthumous*, p. 161). The experiment goes on through all the re-drafting stages – some of the most revelatory developments can arise long after the excitement of the first rush of ideas. Paring down to find the gold where the hidden heart of the poem lies is a balancing act, a tightrope walk between clarity and mystery, with the mystery in a poem often as much a technical affair as much as an imaginative one. A few sharp revisions can change a poem's entire emphasis and argument. Take D. H. Lawrence's revisions to his poem 'Piano', which in his original notebook version closes with this final quatrain (de Sola Pinto, 'Letter-Writer and Craftsman in Verse', 5–34):

> A woman is singing me a wild Hungarian air
> And her arms, and her bosom and the whole of her soul
>   is bare
> And the great black piano is clamouring as my mother's
>   never could clamour
> And the tunes of the past are devoured of this music's
>   ravaging glamour.

The later published version closes quite differently. Much of the key imagery and rhyme is retained, but the action of the woman's singing is radically re-envisioned:

So now it is vain for the singer to burst into clamour
With the great black piano appassionato. The glamour
Of childish days is upon me, my manhood is cast
Down in the flood of remembrance, I weep like a child for
    the past.

(*Complete poems vol. I*, p. 148)

Re-writing is a generative process even at phrase level: interrogating the poem, trying to be emotionally honest and imaginatively alert means also being exacting with the eye and ear. Coleridge speaks eloquently as always about all of this: 'A great Poet... must have the *ear* of a wild Arab listening in the silent Desert; the *eye* of a North American Indian tracing the footsteps of an Enemy upon the Leaves that strew the Forest – ; the *Touch* of Blind Man feeling the face of a darling Child' (*Collected letters II*, p. 810).

## *About dreams*

It's more than coincidence that in the months during which I wrote these two short poems I was also working at close quarters on another visionary world, translating the jewelled fourteenth century dream-elegy *Pearl*, a relay partly of the visions in St John's Revelation and in Dante. 'De Somniis', as the title (borrowed from Philo of Alexandria) describes, is a poem very pointedly about dreams. It draws on early dream theories and the figurative notion of dream as the thing we might most wish, the ambition, the hope we can only imagine realised. 'Why some people like to keep chickens' isn't about dreams, but is perhaps dreamlike in its mode and action. Both draw on an actual dream very clear in my waking mind.

But a dream isn't a poem, it's more like a glass-sided viewing tank onto a fraction of our mind and its preoccupations. Still, there is something direct and unmediated about our experience of dreams which seems very like the imaginative action of poetic composition. The mind has many mansions, not all of which we have a simple key to, and the figure of the dreaming poet has a long history. Keats' question at the close of 'Ode to a nightingale', *Was it a vision or a waking dream?*, resonates across any number of traditions. It's an aspect of Proust's idealised novel, which 'will disturb us in the same way as a dream but a dream that's clearer than those we have when sleeping [*son livre va nous troubler à la façon d'un rêve mais d'un rêve plus clair que ceux que nous avons en dormant*]', (*Du côté de chez Swann*, p. 105). It's the figure haunting Zoran Anchevski's translator who must 'sleep on a pillow/ of someone else's dreams' (*Strategy of defeat*, p. 108), Les Murray's 'dream mind' at work in what he calls a 'true poem' (lecture, *A defence of poetry*), Jo Shapcott's hallucinatory and unsettling *My life asleep*, and a multitude of other work.

The dream at the heart of the *Pearl* elegy – the poem that lies behind the composition of both these poems – is a very literary vision. But it is also a vision with the same heart-stopping power as many actual dreams – the kind of lucid, transformative dream where our apprehension seems utterly clear, experienced at its best with all of Wordsworth's 'glory and freshness', vivid and vital, (*Poems 1807*, p. 523). That vitality is what the imagination seems wonderfully and fearfully to be able to re-create in our waking lives, and language is a key to open doors onto both worlds, imagined as well as recalled, simultaneously. As John Pitcher has said of Edgar's account of the non-existent drop at blind Gloucester's feet in King Lear (in his introduction to The Arden Shakespeare – *The winter's tale*): 'the cliff at Dover is an illusion, but it is more real for us than any real place could be.'

# 3   Kathryn Heyman

## Wood for the trees

The tram makes the sound of the old man's wheezing, grunting up the hill like some half-dead pisshead. Ahead, gaping over me, the forest is dark. The black forest, only it's not black, it's just a load of fucking trees and all I want is to be in the middle of Vaclavske Namesti, in the little red pizza place with steam and talk and huff and some chicks who'll look my way like they want me. Here I am, though, hiking up this stupid fucking hill with this old man. *Mister Co-day.* Behind me, he keeps calling my name, shouting, *slower, please slower*, and then he makes that little *tuktuk* sound with his teeth and I think, Jesus, if I have to hear that sound one more minute, I will take a hammer to his fucking skull. I don't mean to, but that's what I think.

Prague is full of the sound of glass singing and kettle drums, Eastern Europeans singing terrible blooody versions of Bob Fucking Marley and, worse, the great groaner himself, fucking Dylan. *The antspants mafrend is blowy the wind, the antspants is blowy the wind.* Serious. Jesus. I don't know why I came. Some chick, Klara, like the chick from Heidi, the wheelchair chick, asked me to come, to meet her here and, you know, seemed like a good idea and so on. So fucking on.

I caught the coach over. Like that was a good idea. Even at twice the price, three times, flying would have been

45

better. My dad fucked off travelling when I was a kid. Not package-tour shit like everyone does now, he's spent his whole life doing proper travelling: open-air buses in Thailand wearing nappies for his piss; hitch-hiking across Africa, nearly getting killed; villages in Burma, all that shit. He used to send me letters about it, when I was a kid. Once, maybe twice a year, then just postcards: *Hey Cody. Bangalore is full on, the real deal. Had dysentery when I got here. Trekking up the mountains next week with a couple of locals. When you're old enough we'll do it together.* Then the postcards stopped. But, you know, he knew how to travel, my fucking dad. He really did. He was a traveller, not a tourist. Buses, not planes. Flying is for wankers, unless you really have to. You know, to get to the States and shit.

On the coach, I sat behind some guy who took his shoes off and his feet stank of arse crack and hops. I slept with my feet above my head and hoped that this Klara might be bloody worth it.

She sent her father to collect me. He was about three hundred years old, stank of stale goat. He put his hand out, all formal, 'Klara say welcome. She have work emergency. I host you. You come.' I shook his hand back. When he smiled he showed the gaps where teeth should have been but I said *Dobres den* and he said it back and then I looked around for the car but there wasn't one and we had to drag my case up the hill and get on the tram. People wore animal fur hats and earmuffs, gloves so thick you couldn't tell the shape of their hands. I'd brought my coat, a woollen beanie, and my old school gloves with a hole in the thumb. Ice shone on the road but when I saw the tram station I felt a finger of familiarity. It was just like Melbourne, only colder.

All the way up the hill, with the crackling voice on the tram jibbering out station names, I kept my case wedged between my legs. Klara's father sat opposite me, with his hands on his knees, and every time the tram stopped he nodded his head and grinned at me. Now and then he pointed out the window and shouted something enthusiastic, 'Stomovka, there.' Then, so loud it was the sound of someone pushing your eyes out, pop, 'Castle! Castle!' He shook my shoulder with his fat mitty hands, patted them against the window in case I couldn't see. The tram windows were covered with condensation, I couldn't see anything except my own breath but I listened to the rackety sound of the recording announcing the tram stations as we stopped: *Letenskie, Krokoniska, Divorka Sarka.* I turned the sounds of the names over in my head, tried to make their shapes in my mouth. They were like boiled sweets, clicking against my tongue. I leaned over and asked the old man when Klara would be home and he nodded, 'D-yez, d-yez, Klara working'. His breath stank of old curtains and there were little beads of water at the corner of his eyes.

I tried to remember what Klara did for a job. I met her in London, in the middle of the summer, on a five-pound hired deck chair at Regent's Park. She was lying there with her top off – right in the middle of the park – and a Learning Good English book resting across her face. She had a tiny bra on but it had moved sideways so that you could see almost the whole breastegg. She had the best tits I'd ever seen in Regent's Park on a Sunday afternoon. All around her, pensioners and tourists and crap were lying on their hired deck chairs surrounding the lake, all of them tutting like crazy and looking the other way. Some of the

47

old blokes looked right at her but they made sure they had disgusted shapes painted on their mugs. Twisted lips, that kind of thing. The jacketed-up bloke who hired out the chairs was on his way over to her, I swear I saw a little bit of dribble slipping out the side of his mouth, so I tapped the Learning English Good book and said, really quiet, 'I think the guard is coming over here to arrest you. You should put your top on and come with me.'

We spent the afternoon rowing in those pissy little boats they have there and then I took her to that wine bar around the corner, the one that's painted purple so you can't see a thing and we drank two bottles of Californian rosé and then I took her back to mine and got my hands on those tits and I swear we went all night and she screamed so loud that the guy in the flat next to mine actually called the cops. In the morning she tied her hair up in Heidi plaits on top of her head and said 'Oh this is the bloody bad business, my family employer will be calling police I am not home to work.' She kissed me on the nose as if I was a puppy and said, 'That was excellent sex. I have only ten days more of au pair. I come to London for summer only. I am summer au pair.' All of her words were squeezed out, with a little grunt before them, a *mmmnnyyah*, which made her sound Russian, or like she was in pain. She said, 'You come to see me in Prague, in my town? I have apartment.' Then she clapped her hands together as if she was a four-year-old and shouted 'You come after Christmas. For New Year, yes?' I shrugged, because New Year was a long way off and also I wanted it to look like I had plans for New Year. 'It is very cultural. My country will become two. Slovakia and Czech, no longer Czechoslovakia. This is history.' She flicked her tongue across her lips and I said yes because I liked the idea of more of that excellent sex. And history, of course.

Klara wasn't there when we got to the flat, either. And the flat, it turned out, was part of her parents' house in a line of houses that made me think of the man who walked a crooked mile and lived in a crooked house. I had a book with that in it when I was a kid and the picture was of this bent-over codger in a red suit, standing outside a narrow four-storey brick house, toppling sideways. Klara's dad was like the crooked man but with nothing as funky as a red suit, and the house, Jesus. The whole street stretched up on an angle of about eighty degrees. Straight up, I mean. The tram ran past the outside, practically touched the front door. So Klara had an apartment on the ground floor, and her parents had one upstairs. Cosy.

The apartment had concrete walls and cream carpet on the floor. The old man bobbed his little head at me and made a sicky sucking sound with his teeth – it was the first time I heard his trademark *tuktuk* – and then he said, 'Klara say you stay here, we take special care for you. Be host.' He stood in the doorway smiling at me, with my grey backpack all tattered at his feet, nodding. But when I asked him when, when would Klara be back, then he stopped nodding. 'Soon. She come for you soon. She say very sorry. Emergency in hospital.'

Doctor. That's what she did for a job. I saw her four times in London. Each time, she talked while I pulled her clothes off, unplaited her hair, pushed her against the wall. Some of her babble must have gone in, without me noticing it.

When the door closed behind the old man a pebble of concrete fell off the wall and made a dead sound on the carpet. I walked around the apartment, touching the walls, letting the nylon of the carpet rub against my toes and I thought about the way she'd flicked herself around in my flat, like a cobra, hair zinging across my face. Jesus. I'd spent almost four months thinking about getting here, imagining her waiting outside the coach, waving a sign with my name on it. Mixed in with the arse-crack smell of the sockless feet on the coach, I'd thought about her pulling me into her apartment, pulling me down onto the ground, and then taking me out into the wild streets of Prague.

I felt so lonely I thought I might wank myself to fucking death.


It was dark when she got home and I'd been lying on her bed in my long johns, rolling in and out of sleep, waiting for the moment when she'd burst through the door. She clambered on top of me and tugged at me, her hair flicking across my face just the way I'd imagined. Making bloody history, all right. She had to work the next day, and the next, and the one after that. Each morning, she rolled herself against me and said, 'My father wishes to show you our city today,' and each morning I said yes, okay, because all I could think of was pleasing her. She'd got me, somehow.

The old man marched me out each morning, tapping on my door, and standing on the threshold bobbing eagerly. 'Good morning Mister Co-day. I show you our palace today.' Palace, or park, or museum. We caught the tram into the city and I watched the backpackers my age, clumping in groups behind café windows. Sometimes, he lurked at a respectful distance. He stood at the end of Karlov Most, the bridge that stretched from the castle, waving to me while I wandered past the world's worst fucking buskers. In the big square, he pointed to the place that some kid had set fire to himself to protest against the Russians and I thought I might just do the same if someone would give me a light. At night, Klara came back to the apartment and we ate dinner with the old man and I worked so hard at being polite I thought my face might split in two. We skated on the pond outside the apartments, with the curve of the church behind us and her father waiting on the edge, his face wrapped in Klara's scarf. We went to the opera, the three of us: her father clapping in the stalls and turning to me with his face pink from happiness, shouting in my ear, 'We still have this, as good as London, yes?' And I nodded and clapped along and it wasn't what I'd imagined and it wasn't as good as London and it wasn't like being a real fucking traveller at all.

But history came, whether or not I wanted it to. New Year's Eve, the great separation of two countries. We ate dinner with the old man and then walked through the square and Klara made me say the name of it again and again: *Vaclavske Namesti, Vaclavske Namesti* and each time I said it she squealed and said it was so cute my silly accent but the fact is I said it just the way they said it on the tram station announcements. Someone let some fireworks off at midnight, some twirling bungers that spiraled across the cobblestones, taking a newspaper with them. Klara smiled and said, 'There. Now we are two countries. Good.' We went back to the apartment and played strip poker but it wasn't enough to make it seem like I'd been part of something big.

She was back at work three days later, with the old man tapping at the door of the apartment, feeling obliged to

51

take me on guided tours of the city and me feeling obliged to go. Konopiste Castle, Stormovka, the Jewish Quarter, St Vitus Cathedral. Today, some fucking forest.

The tram driver jangles a bell as it wheezes off and the old man gestures to the trees. 'The forest.' Yes, I say. I see that. He says, 'We walk through, up hill, there, and collect tram on other side. Very old gates. Good.' Then he makes his little tuk-tuk sound and I breathe in deep thinking about how I'd imagined it, this whole trip, this time – being part of history, being part of all that excellent sex. We set off, huffing up the narrow path, while he points out every single fucking tree and its inhabitants to me and all I want is to be quiet, to be alone to be part of something, something big. He keeps huffing and pointing out the rock over there and the re-winged, lower spotted, half-fucking-nosed bat-robin in the corner and I start walking just a bit faster, just to stay ahead of him, just to stop myself shouting at him to shut the fuck up.

*Mister Co-day, slow down. I show you.* He huffs and tuks but he keeps marching just behind me, keeps to his duty as guide and host, pointing out the path, the sky, the walls of the star-shaped chateau that was built by someone or bloody other and we can go and see it just over yonder. I pick up the pace a bit more, just so I can walk ahead, that's all, just so I can stop hearing him, just for a minute, just for a day. He picks it up too, so that he's trotting beside me, wheezing, 'Klara happy you come to Prague. Very happy. I take care. Host you for her. I love to show you my country.' Yes, I say, I know, and I start to jog, to pound along the path with the darkness of the forest over me and the wheezing of the old man beside me. His wheezing is louder and louder while he tries to stay right there beside me. The wheezing catches, and he calls out, 'Mister – hurting – Co – I –' and I hear a sort of gasp and a pop and that tuk sound, I keep hearing it, that tuktuk tuktuk and I just can't stand it, I can't stand having it right there all the time and even though I hear the scrape of legs and skin on gravel, I keep running until I am pounding against the rocks hard and so fast that I can't hear anything except my own breath, my own heart.

Sunlight starts to filter in through the trees as I pass some high walls. The tuk-tuk sound has stopped in my head. Some hard pebble is rattling in my chest, so I slow down, let the sweat trickle down my neck. By the time I pass near the edge of the woods, I've stopped panting but there's a wet triangle at the top of my chest. The pounding head-cracking sound in my head is replaced by the bird whistles outside, real sounds. Footsteps crunch towards me on the path and I watch, head down, as the feet come into view. Nikes. I look up, nod at the guy walking towards me, hair covered in a bright red beanie. He nods back, says 'Hi' in an American accent. Not even an attempt to speak Czech. Jesus, I think, it's just fucking rude. He crunches away down the path, past me, towards the old man and I watch him as he gets swallowed up by the trees.

I take the water bottle out of my rucksack and skull it down. Then I just stand there, on my own in the middle of the woods, with no idea what the fuck to do next. I don't even know where the tram stop is. Barely five minutes pass before I hear the American, down in the woods, shouting his head off. First it's just a shout, wordless, then 'Hey! Hey!' And then it changes to 'Help! Someone!' His voice is muffled against the trees but he keeps shouting,

Helphelp, Helpsomeonehelp, and he doesn't stop until he sees me running back down the path towards him.

The old man is flat on the ground, face down, with his hands beside him like he'd tried to break his fall. The American is on his knees, hand on the old man's back, and he looks up at me like I'm his mother. 'Can. You. Help?' He speaks really slow in case I'm Czech or some other kind of foreign and when I say I'll try, he's so relieved to hear me speak English that I think he almost pisses himself. I kneel down, and to be honest, I think I piss myself a bit too, maybe more than piss, because for a minute I think the old man isn't breathing but then I hear a gurgle down in his throat and I say to the American, 'Roll him over, carefully.' Between us we roll the old man over. Bits of gravel have dug into his face where he fell. I try not to look at them. We lift the old man and hobble up the path, carrying him between us, one arm over each of our shoulders. Every so often the old man gives a little moan but we keep walking. We're careful with him. The American seems to know where he's going, so I let him lead the way.

'Jeez,' he says, 'I was lucky you were there. He's light, but I'd struggle to carry him alone, you know?'

I say I do know.

He huffs a bit, then says, 'We need to get him to hospital. There are usually taxis waiting on the gate side of the park. Have been, anyway, both times I've been before.'

I say I've never been in a Prague taxi.

He says his name's Nick and that he'd shake my hand if he could. He says I'm a real good Samaritan.

The old man moans again, but his eyes are closed and I can't tell if he's properly conscious or not. Blood drips on his chin, from the gravel. If I weren't holding him up I think

I'd be sick. We struggle up to the wide gates that form an entrance to the woods and Nick's right, there are two taxis right there, like yellow-tipped angels. The driver doesn't even shift his arse to help us get the old man into the back seat, though. He's a fat bastard with a fag hanging out of his mouth with a line of ash as long as his finger and he speaks not one word of English. We shout Hospital, Hospital. Nothing. Nick pulls a phrase book out of his rucksack, flicks through it and leans over the back of the seat, pointing to the picture. Fucking phrasebooks. I've never bothered.

We skid outside the hospital, and this time the driver hops to it a bit, heaving his fat arse out of the seat to shout a long list of instructions to a grey-haired nurse walking out of the front doors. Nick helps me wrangle the old man out then slides himself back into the taxi. He says, 'Do you mind if I don't wait? I was supposed to meet my friends at the chateau in the woods. We're all staying in town, at the hostel.'

The nurse has managed to get hold of an ancient-looking wheelchair, and she and the driver gently fold the old man into it. Nick shakes my hand, as if we're old mates. 'We'll be at the pizza place in Wenceslas Square later. Come for a drink. If you want.'

I don't want. As the taxi speeds off, the nurse points me towards the hospital door, patting me on the head. She says something incomprehensible, then marches off towards the car park, wrapping a moose-brown cape about her shoulders. Inside, I give them Klara's name, and she runs to me, her sensible Eastern bloc doctor shoes slipping on the linoleum. She kisses me before she takes her father away, and her tongue whips like a cobra. *Thank you*, she whispers, *you save my father's life.*

He remembers nothing. Just his heart, aching, then the fall. Next: the hospital. Me by his side, and his clever doctor daughter with make-up tear-streaked on her cheeks. She asks how I carried him and I say, 'He ain't heavy, he's your father.'

I stay with her for an extra week and when I leave, I hug the old man for almost as long as I hug Klara. All the way back to London, on the coach, I frame the story, the way I'll tell it. I try to remember the details: the castle, the tramstop names, the sounds of the words. I want to keep it as one of my travellers' tales to tell years from now, the story of how I was a part of something big, how I saved somone's life while history was being made.

'I was a traveller, not a tourist' I'll say. 'Full on.'

The real fucking deal.

# Navigating the dark woods of fiction

Like most Australians of my generation (X, if you're asking), I spent my early twenties carting a backpack from youth hostel to seedy *pensione*, often hosted by kind strangers or friends-of-friends-of-friends, caught in a loop of uncertain charity and courtesy. On the eve of the separation of Czechoslovakia into two nations, I stood in the square where Jan Palach had set fire to himself in 1969 and watched a spatter of fireworks in the square. Like the somewhat obnoxious narrator in 'Wood for the trees', I had travelled to Prague in the hope of being part of something, of witnessing history. During that same visit an elderly acquaintance escorted me, courteously showing off the architectural and cultural marvels of that extraordinary city while I sulked, waiting to be free to find some more 'authentic' experience.

In *The ancestor game* novelist Alex Miller writes of a young boy, 'What he feared and envied was the blind man's ability to dwell at will within the past and to re-arrange it – as if every moment that has ever been continues to exist somewhere, enriched by subsequent events. He dreaded the consequences of the storyteller's ability to recover and to reconsider those moments, and to offer them up as judgments.' This is surely the lifeblood of writing, this desire and ability to revisit and reclaim buried moments and reshape them. The image of my sulky, ungrateful self being patiently and graciously hosted by this man has, I think, tugged at my conscience for all the years since and somehow, at last, fiction has enabled me to assuage my discomfort.

'We cannot post ourselves back in time,' writes historian Inga Clendinnen in 'The history question: who owns the past?' (1-72). And yet that is precisely what the writer of fiction attempts to do, while recognising all the time that it's nothing more or less than a literary effect. In Rachel Ward's feature film *Beautiful Kate* the tagline is 'the past is always present'. To be provocative or, if you like, to be historically crude, there is no such thing as the past. We make it up each time we attempt in our imaginations to revisit a moment in time that has passed irrevocably into the darkness of Never Again. Who better than a writer to point out that past, present and future are at the very least the creations of literary style – they are tenses. In fiction as in life, we revisit the past in order to establish who we are now by examining and arguing over, and describing in words the shape cast by the shadow of our present form.

In 'Wood for the trees' I wanted to play with this idea of history as a mere backdrop to an individual's story, as a way of reflecting on the narcissism of a certain sort of travelling, and of a certain sort of youth. The story I intended to write began, the way stories often do, as something else entirely. I had carved out a clever little plot, containing a whole iceberg of history and subtext, but however much I trimmed and poked and baked, I couldn't make it cook. Each time I sat down to the story, this nasty little viper voice came into my head, and with it, the image of a forest and an old man and a young traveller's desire to be part of history.

Writing, before all, is communication. It is communication with oneself and one's inner life even before it is communication with another. More broadly than that even, writing achieves something. It externalises what was previously internal and half-recognised. It allows thought to create itself by leaving a trail. T.S. Eliot captured this moment of existential frustration in *The love song of J. Alfred Prufrock*: 'That is not it at all, / That is not what I meant, at all'. Whatever else it is, writing is also a tool for getting beyond the frustration, a means of self-recognition. 'The little girl had the making of a poet in her who, being told to be sure of her meaning before she spoke, said: 'How can I know what I think till I see what I say?' (Graham Wallas, *The art of thought*, quoted in Davidson, 'Knowing one's own mind'). For a novelist, it is tempting to see a short story as a sprint, a tiny fraction of a whole. In fact, when I trace the genesis of 'Wood for the trees', the image which comes to mind is one of distillation: the slow drip of a whiskey still, waiting until the time is right. A novel begins with a grand idea, a concept wanting to be explored. Short fiction, for me, begins differently, always with a moment. Indeed, with 'Wood for the trees' it was the case that I didn't know what I thought until I saw what I said.

Some years after my backpacking adventures, I remembered the annoyance I'd felt with the kindly host. I know my worst shadows, my ugliest feelings: I'm a novelist, after all, and to inhabit uncomfortable feelings, to give them light, is part of the job. So it was a small step to imagine the feeling of annoyance being so great that I wanted to run away from the man, ceasing to have any concern for any feelings but one's own. So then I had a story waiting to be written. Several notebooks attest to its existence. In 1998, in my graph-paper, round-cornered Moleskine notebook, I wrote: 'Short story. Girl walking with old man. Prague forest. She runs, makes him run too. He dies.' The pale, barely formed idea was transferred dutifully to other notebooks, embarrassing in its nakedness. But each time I glanced at it, those words, something else, however slight, formed. The forest, the square, the sound of the man. This is the way fiction works: it waits until you are ready. Perhaps it's like growing root vegetables, with so much work going on beneath the surface. And like gardening, occasional tending is required before the harvest. Nothing onerous – plucking off some insects, clearing a weed or two, providing water. With fiction (because we have now reached the end of my gardening knowledge) the waiting is less weeding and more showing up, periodically revisiting the idea. Listening and waiting, that's what this is. Alan Garner writes about this process in *The voice that thunders*, when he writes of taking three decades for his masterpiece, *Strandloper*, to fully reveal itself.

For a decade, that was all I had: a small image of the young woman walking too fast, so fast that the old man crumpled. I had no idea what the story was actually *about*, though. Nonetheless, bidden or unbidden, the old man and the girl bubbled away in the whiskey-still of my subconscious until I sat down to write another story, a lighter, brighter kind of story.

This other story, the one I thought I'd be writing about, was a narrative thread abandoned from my current novel. It pleased me, the thought that the girl I'd cast aside from my novel would find a home in her own story. That one had travel in it, too: an airport, a departure, a prayer and a lie. And, it turned out, no zing. Timing is part of the mystery of the creative process. It was time for the old man to have his moment.

I wasn't sure until I began writing what gender my narrator was. I was sure, though, of the final image: the narrator, running, blood pounding in his ears, while the old man lies in the dirt. It was only when I'd written what I thought was the final line that I realised what the story is, at its heart, about. I'd thought I was writing just about callousness, about the awkwardness of obligation pitted against the desire for isolation. In fact, I was writing, I realised suddenly, about the greed of travel itself, the lustful quality of travel-for-travel's sake. In that light, the context of place became critical.

In a great piece of fiction, the setting is much more than a lifeless backdrop. The house in Tim Winton's *Cloudstreet*, for example, becomes a character in its own right, as ramshackle and lovable as Fish Lamb himself. Or, another house, Wuthering Heights in Emily Brontë's novel of the same name – ramshackle in its own way, but far from lovable. Brooding and mysterious, the house becomes a character and also reflects Heathcliffe's character. In Peter Carey's *Parrot and Olivier in America*, the whole nation becomes a key player in the narrative. On a miniature scale, when the young Parrot describes the secret printer's room, he piles metaphor upon metaphor as the child attempts to capture the feeling of the room, to impale it upon the page. The room is an ark, no it's a fur coat, it's golden, warm, an animal – he shifts around like a photographer, trying this angle and that, until, satisfied, he returns to the first image: an ark. In 'Wood for the trees' I wanted to make place an intrinsic part of the narrative, a player in the story – at least within the story the protaganist tells himself. Place is key for me. Like Winton (Stegar, 'It's a risky business', 28), I need to know where a story is before I can settle down to the world of it. I need to feel the air, the rocks beneath my feet. Here was the problem with this particular story though: in Cody, I had created a narrator who is so utterly self-absorbed that he is effectively unable to properly notice his environment, except as artifice, a prop to his own fictional future narratives.

Why him, then? Given that I *consciously* wanted to evoke Prague at a particular moment in history, why choose a narrator who is unable to fully describe the world he walks through? In response to my own question, I draw on the words of Virginia Woolf in the essay 'Mr Bennett and Mrs. Brown':

> And when I asked myself, as your invitation to speak to you about modern fiction made me ask myself, what demon whispered in my ear and urged me to my doom, a little figure rose before me – the figure of a man, or of a woman, who said, 'My name is Brown. Catch me if you can.' Most novelists have the same experience. Some Brown, Smith, or Jones comes before them and says in the most seductive and charming way in the world, 'Come and catch me if you can.' And so, led on by this will-o'-the-wisp, they flounder through volume after volume, spending the best years of their lives in the pursuit, and receiving for the most part very little cash in exchange.

Here, the place itself – Prague at a particular time – did some of its own will-o'-the-wisping, certainly. But I could not leave him, that abhorrent narrator in his ill-fitting long johns – and, as uncomfortable as I found it (and I did), I could not remove myself from his company, nor articulate why he had claimed a space in my imagination.

In Woolf's essay, she goes on to describe a passing encounter with a real life Mrs Brown: a stranger on a train, intriguing for a reason that the novelist is unable to articulate, even to herself. This inability to articulate the reason seems to me to be a critical part of the process of creating fiction. Articulation, indeed, should come only through the process of creation. That is, we understand the why of the call – why this character and not another – once we have pursued it. Because, I would suggest, the mystery is critical to the process of creative unknowing, and creative unknowing is the alchemical ingredient of fiction. It isn't enough to map out a path through the dark woods of fiction. In order to fully engage with the act of creation that fiction requires, it is necessary to first be utterly lost.

# 4   Philip Gross

*Cave diver in the deep reach*

### In the first chamber
even before he'd slipped his wet-suit on
he found
     in the show cave
the gift stall and knick-knacks and shiver of flash
and people posing by the famous stalagmites
     *(The Troll And His Child,*
     *The Bubblegum Burp,*
     *The Frozen Angel)* and
the still pool, shading deeper, and
     the warning sign
          that he would go beyond.


### In the second chamber
he found a disembodied voice
had followed him, high up and trapped
in its clattery reverb,
     trying to detain
some tripper on the hanging walkway with its tale
of the hag they drove out from the bounds of the village,
with fire, like a beast,
     drove her into the hills,
into the deep-and-darkest cleft of their own dreams.

**In the third:**
      on a high ledge, moss
with fey light of its own,
        a rusted lunch box, a flint scraper,
        three small vertebrae, a smoke stain,
        and a blusher-tint of ochre
on the cave roof stencilling a maker's hand…
        All that and a ring-pull glinting
        like abandoned treasure,
and a slightly-yellowed could it be a cave bear's tooth?

**In the fourth chamber**
he found the roof too low,
almost, for him to surface. Something brushed his face
— pale root-hairs hung like a wiry cloud,
and cobweb-floss
        tacked up by bodiless spiders
like the loose connections
           of the inside of a sleeping brain.

**In the fifth:**
      a leakage of grey daylight
through a dizzy-upward chasm in the roof,
drips as heavy as chain-mail,
      and the buckled fender
of what might have been a classy Porsche
tipped down a pothole, evidence
      disposed of. Someone

high above had listened for its falling clatter
to be laid to rest. Maybe they still did
      waking in the (every) night.


*In the sixth:*
      no consolation
in being almost entirely sure
that the s-shaped whip-flick of light
was his torch beam in the ripples
as he surfaced — that there was no such thing
as a colourless cave-snake
swimming this deep, hunting using senses
he could scarcely guess at,
trapped as he was in that of sight.


*In the seventh chamber*
beyond the longest tightest sump
      he found, even there
the air moved slightly. There was still a *to* and *from*,
      a something that '*knows* something,'
he caught himself thinking, and blushed.
      Had he spoken out loud?
        Had it heard?

### In the eighth chamber

he found some relief in counting—eight,
one more than seven—as he used to in bed,
aged one year more than four and (as long
as he never lost count or stopped counting)
>              not, not afraid, not afraid of the dark.


### In the ninth chamber:

>              a cleft

in the blank wall the shape of lightning,
black,
>              as if the hill had prised itself apart

and was holding it, trembling with the effort,
just enough
>              (*quick, now*, it seemed to say...

*or never*) to let the river squeeze through
out from its deep captivity
and (as if it wanted something
in exchange) for him
>              to wriggle though.


### In the tenth:

>              an X

scratched where the walls
and ceiling and black water came to one
blank point: a *No Admittance* where words had run out,
a furthest point, a record, that someone
had wanted to sign, or sign
off, and then found
they'd forgotten their name.

*In the eleventh chamber:*
                a frozen cloudburst
of stalactites, hailstones held in their fall
through an endless dimension,
like spacetime on ice, the way that God
might see it or we might,
                our little life-
lines parallel and glittering,
if we had a place to stand outside it all.


*In the twelfth:*
                the stream so thin now
that it must be near — the source,
as far from the surface world
as the headwaters of the Amazon.
That's when he found
                his air gauge
nudging empty
                and he did the calculation.
He did the sum again.
                A fifty-fifty chance.

He went on.

# Caves of making, and the making of a cave

### *Accounting for the poem*

Headwaters... Dewponds, sources, springs ... Cave country: limestone landscape, in my case that of the Mendips, with underground streams and swallets where a lost dog might drop without trace and, in one local story, come out of a cave mouth panting, twenty miles away...

This is where I am starting, acknowledging these place-associations as a way to put this poem in its place. It is a poem neither finished nor consciously work-in-progress, unless returning to explore it here is a part of its progress. Its process, at least... and writing *process* is (discuss!) the one unique thing that Creative Writing studies as a discipline. My urge to write this feels like evidence of the poem's uncompleted life. The dialogue of write-reflect-and-write-again is still under way.

If this was a literary study of a text, I might be starting in the wrong place, with the wrong material – a poem unachieved, in the sense of not yet having separated from its writer or the writer from it. With my partial, partisan, all-too-implicated author's view, I might be the wrong person to account for it. But to students and teachers of Creative Writing, and to anyone interested in the way creation happens inside us, the margin of error is a fruitful place to be. As evolution depends on errors, the mis-copying of DNA codes, human inventiveness requires its accidents, and unachieved work can open spyholes into that nearly-there-ness which for creative work is a necessary state, a state of *possibility*.

The writer's inside view, too – partial, fallible and still up to the armpits in the making – is material. Not that we have to take the writer at his or her word. As in any committed reading of creative work, the reader will test this story of one text's creation against their own experience, and against the self-reports of other writers too.

The use of the word 'story' here is deliberate. When we *account for* a poem it is not in the book-keeping sense of drawing up the sum; we *give an account of* it, a narrative. What I am about to say about this poem and its process may be a fiction, a creation myth. Any myth, anthropologically studied, may be as revealing of the process, of its own creation in a culture, as about what it purports to explain.

In the culture of writing poetry, and in its teaching, an uneasy but creative balance holds between the idea of rhetoric and that of reader response. On the one hand, the art and skill of the writer persuades a reader into the experience on offer; on the other, we increasingly acknowledge that each reader will flesh out the signs we make with their own sensations and associations. (At the level of theory, the debate between the two can be fierce. In practice, most writers know that enlisting your reader's active and imaginative engagement is an act of wooing in itself, the offer of just enough satisfactions to make them want more.) This chapter is no different. It does not claim to have the last word on the writing of the poem it considers; like the poem itself, it wants to be read creatively, and it hopes to be read in good faith. It assumes too that the web of intertextuality that gives our writing resonance and substance is not restricted to 'texts' that are published or written or in any way created. Alongside the intertext, the study of a poem's process includes *intra*-text, material inside the writer, not or not yet written, maybe not quite knowable, but generative nonetheless.

## A creation myth

'Cave diver in the deep reach' is not, to my knowledge, a poem about writing a poem. (That kind of reflexivity has a bad name among non-specialist readers, though that negative response may overlook one fact: for many poets who live consciously in language the business of making becomes a metaphor, not a replacement, for the fundamental things of life.) Even so, the imagery implies the possibility; this is not just a cave but a cave system, a process in itself, and the course the diver follows leads deeper in, upstream. The question of a source cannot help but suggest itself.

'Suggests *itself*...?' Yes. Even a partially achieved poem is its own subculture, full of cross-reference and implication; what holds its elements in some cohesion is, at least implicitly, a story of itself. As in writing a novel, where the writer feels him or herself to be 'discovering' a character's back story or motivations (rather than constructing them) a certain critical mass of ingredients in a poem will begin to make suggestions by an inner logic of their own. The logic of this poem is a journey leading... where? *Where* is another question, as we will see.

The writer, too, is operating in their own self-subculture, a story of what kind of writer they are and where their work is leading. Where the self-stories of the poem and of the writer conflict, interesting interference patterns can ensue (Gross, 'Giving houseroom to our waifs and strays', 33–40). In many ways the Cave Diver poem seems mis-fitting, difficult to 'own' among my other poems; writing this chapter is a way of owning it, possible because my story of my writing self includes myself as writing teacher and investigator, who values his misfits for clues they might hold.

This poem seems to be a narrative. Its sections/stanzas are numbered; they have order; it is leading somewhere, or so it invites us to think. It is a journey, the oldest story-shape of them all, and it seems to deploy the story-maker's techniques of challenge, jeopardy, suspense, relief and escalation as it leads us further from the world outside. Instead of out into the world, as in adventure, this journey seems to be leading its hero back, inside himself and back in time.

At this point you might ask the writer: was this his intention? Did the poem always have this structure? Both answers are No. Early notebooks would show that it cohered out of a cloud or crowd of coexisting images which slowly jostled into order. Did he consent to this order? Certainly. The subculture of the poem itself implied that they were leading somewhere, relating as it does to a whole world's story-culture round it. Whether you regard that story-shape as laid down culturally or psychologically or even deeper, physiologically, in our genes, the idea of the Quest was ready and waiting for the elements to flow into its suggestive shape.

### The things of which we ourselves are made

In writing, says David Jones, 'one is trying to make a shape out of the very things of which one is oneself made' (*The anathemata*, p. 10). Leave the shape aside for now; what can we know about the source materials that have been shaped? A text-based literary study will be alert for intertextual references, placing it in a web of other writers' works. A more process-centred study will include the traces left by the writer in unpublished form and, if they are still living, interviews. To this, the self-observing writer can add what is currently known, or half-known, to themselves.

Here I am, or a child who appears to be me, in Kents Cavern, Torquay. Circumstantial evidence tells me I am five. It's not much of a theme park, by modern standards, but it's the sight of a real prehistoric cave bear's tooth that gives me dreams that night. Fifty years on, I find that tooth in the Cave Diver poem, not much of a mention but it does provide the closing, hanging words of section three. As I look now, I notice that the equivalent closing words of the adjacent sections are 'dreams' and 'sleeping brain' and 'lay awake / night after night'.

A child, but older (I may be ten) I'm closer to the landscape of the poem – visiting first the Cheddar caves, then the more theatrically presented Wookey Hole. The story of the witch, the walkway and the gift shop can be sourced from there, as can the crowd-pleasing names of stalactite formations. (The names I play with here are my own, though faithful to the genre.) All those are incidentals in my memory; at its centre is a single inexplicit glimpse of the deepening, darkening pool beyond which, we were told, only divers could go. It is only a glimpse, but it is undeniably the centre of gravity, the high-pressure point of a half-appalling, fascinated feeling tone.

In my teens, I am a climber, genuinely risking life and limb on rock faces. Some friends suggest potholing, and I shudder. This, I know then, corresponds to my worst nightmare, which is of crawling through a narrow and narrowing tunnel, towards an opening I can see but never reach, until I can no longer move. (Birth trauma? There is no evidence, incidentally, that mine was problematic ... though maybe trauma comes as standard.) Just as I consider that I might go down and face this fear, I hear some boys in the youth hostel kitchen telling the tale of a friend of a friend who died potholing. He slipped and wedged deeper; in a state of panic, they say with plausible authority, muscles dilate; add rigor mortis, and his body could not be recovered, so they simply sealed the cave.

Years later again, another passing anecdote falls into the gravitational field of this memory. A friend of a friend is telling why he gave up serious cave diving; he was in the support party for a diver who ran out of air ... not suddenly, but at some point realised that he had insufficient air to get back, and chose to wait calmly, talking to the support team on his walkie-talkie, rather than die struggling in a sump. To be underground is one thing; underwater underground is quite another, and that 'calmly' was the twist that sealed it all in place.

This much I know: I received those impressions. Whether the stories are true may be beside the point. Of course, the material no more *accounts for* the poem than the contents of a fridge account for tonight's supper. I had thought before about writing that last anecdote, as prose, quite likely as teenage horror. Other factors account for why I did not write it then, and why much later in this poem, in some form and scarcely knowing it, I did.

### Ghosts in the cave

Who would think of using such material for a children's poem? I did not, but it was a process of assembling a children's poetry collection that brought this poem about. *Off road to everywhere* assembles poems I have written for, with, after or alongside writing workshops with school children over fifteen years. It contains several sequences in which each section is a variation on a theme – a series of imaginary boats made of impossible substances, a range of voices given to small never-before-noticed details in a room, a set of buildings or places that embody your impression of the thing called *poetry*... In each case, half the game is in the breeding of endless possibilities, often out loud in a group, and how one idea stimulates another to be as different as it can be. The published poems are by me, but could come with the phrase 'Serving Suggestion Only' on the packet; they are designed to suggest the reader-writer's possibilities, not to be the last word.

One of these poetry places came in the image of the cave. When that short piece suggested more – another cave, another chamber – it seemed possible that a whole sub-sequence might be under way. It had become a congregation of ten parts or so, and had a place in the draft of the book, before the shape, the journey that I mentioned earlier, began to emerge. As it did, I saw where the journey was leading – where, it now occurred to me, it had been leading all along. Even as someone whose children's poetry is known for being anything but condescending, I realised that it was leading somewhere younger readers might not need to go.

This had not been a foregone conclusion. Childhood is there in warp and weft of the piece, and not only in the opening section with its brief but knowing nod to children's humour. I never imagined the cave diver to be a child, but the effect of the darkness on him, in the sixth, seventh and eighth sections, seems to be regression. Leaving behind the clutter of modern, adult life strips him back to childhood, though not of a comfortable or comforting kind. If the ninth section hints (in hindsight, this is; no such idea was consciously formed in my mind) at a kind of rebirthing, it is not a new birth but exchanging life for... what? Not immediately or exactly death. There might be wonder in it, too, beyond the point of losing one's identity. Reading this now, I sense the shape of strange and venerable myth-journeys – the Tibetan or the Egyptian or, in this case, the Somerset Book of the Dead.

At this stage the poem had the twelve sections published here. The twelfth, however, *felt* penultimate. It might have been the lingering weight of my first assumption that this was intended for a children's book. Younger readers are notoriously unsatisfied by open endings in fiction, unless of course a sequel is clearly implied. From a certain age the closure of a sad or wistful ending can be contemplated, but not outright uncertainty. So one of the ghosts that haunt this published text is that of a section thirteen:

*In the thirteenth chamber*
with no surface he could reach he found
himself        alone
and as his torch beam fluttered
and went out   he found he knew
        (these telling blanks now in the hiss
of breathing)  who
                how much        how
        slight   and yet
what mattered
        In the darkness, it was very clear.

Was this enough, to give the protagonist the comfort of a small enlightenment? It was still a death scene. The section stood for a while, as I tried to decide whether this comfort was too little or too much. It might be both – no real consolation, yet the danger of an almost Romantic idealisation of the 'easeful death'. If so, two imbalances did not make a balance. Nor did the blanks between the words feel as 'telling' as I had hoped. (I know now where they came from – not from the world of this poem but from the poems I was starting to write about my father's deepening aphasia (*Deep Field*).) One of those poems, with blanks written in mid line like this, came shortly after; it was the one, I realised, that was nudging at the edges of this thirteenth section, and as soon as I saw that, the section fell away.)

Before it disappeared, another would-be-ending had appeared in my notebook, like an epilogue:

> *(And there, in these*
> *interstices between us,*
> *in Schrödinger's box, he is,*
> *he is not, he is dead and alive.*
>
> *Dear reader, if*
> *we work together*
> *we could reach him.*
> *We could reach him if we try.)*

It hung there, in those brackets and italics, in its meta-space, for a short while, until a poet-editor whose judgment I respect said just enough for me to realise that what she was about to say I already knew: this nod to Reader-response theory was a sleight of hand and worse, a safety mechanism; in exchange for dismantling whatever willing suspension of disbelief the reader had been pleased to grant me, it gained little but a knowing wink.

*The shape of the spaces between*

The gaps between words in the discarded section serve to highlight the fact that the whole poem makes a feature of the spaces between words – especially, between its stanzas. So far I have referred to it simply as 'a poem'. Is it one? Or is it twelve small poems in a sequence? It sets out to blur that difference with its visual clues. Yes, each section is a single block of words (although the stepped line breaks push that impression almost to the edge). They can be read as stanzas in a single poem. They are not divided by an asterisk or other conventional sign. Nor are they numbered, though the game immediately becomes to make a numbered list in their first lines. The italics and bold type of those first lines make them reach towards the function of sub-titles... but they insist on being part of the first sentence, with no more pause than any other line-break, and often the stepped break in the line insists that rhythmically they are part of a single, if interrupted, flow.

In short, they want it both ways. They create a space between their sections longer and deeper than a single poem would allow – as long, if you like, as the struggle in the sump between one chamber and the next. But they insist, in much the same way that the stepped lines do, that the same movement forward runs on through.

The form of a poem is part of its message. This sequence is both about and is bred by the idea of each new chamber being a different 'take' – a strategy which invites the writer to work through a range of styles and shapes and sounds. This is a method known to many a student and most teachers in the world of writing workshops, often presented in the teasing, provocative form of Wallace Stevens' 'Thirteen ways of looking at a blackbird', a sequence of brief verses which make startling leaps of register and tone of voice, returning always to the single, simplest point of reference: the blackbird (Stevens, *Harmonium*).

Stevens' poem comes from the early twentieth century, a time of experiment with poetic forms, though it also picks up the flavour of the *haiku*, the classic Oriental seventeen-syllable form that conveys an instantaneous sensation. It prefigures a more recent concern with juxtaposing voices, tones and registers. If, in the meaning of the Italian word, a 'stanza' is a room, then we are challenged to make each room a pleasing or unsettling shift of ambience. It is a thoroughly empowering game for learning writers, inviting them to let go of their apparent certainties about what they want to be saying and how the poem will speak. It lies behind the now-you-try-it sequences for young writers in *Off road to everywhere*. But all of us are learning writers, I would hope.

A Blackbird sequence does not impose an order (though I am sure that Stevens used both thought and instinct in the way he set his on the page). 'Cave diver in the deep reach' spells an order out... and here is the paradox: working in this form, prizing the absence of narrative order in a sequence, creates a kind of matrix. Its separate elements are fluid, floating on the space between. All the easier, then, for them to be receptive to the other patterns that are working in the culture round us, in the language, in our minds... The spaces between separate stanzas/sections in this poem were designed to encourage difference (and dialogue) between its own different tones and attitudes. In the process, they also resonate with voices from outside. Each space might be, in W. H. Auden's words, 'a cave of making.' That resonant phrase invites the reader, the critic or fellow writer to listen for echoes of their own.

Like iron filings in a magnet, the free-floating images and feelings find themselves arranging into archetypal patterns, like the quest, the night-journey or the sojourn in the underworld.

*An encounter with Orpheus*

The value of unfinished work – work at that stage of nearly-there-ness – is that it continues to reach for connections, sometimes in spite of you. Because not quite a definitive statement, it still has the feeling of a dialogue. This sequence had rested for a year or more before quite a different encounter brought it back to light... or rather back into the dark where it belonged.

During 2009 and 2010 a group of poets and poetry critics based in Wales had been meeting as part of the BorderLines research project which aims to investigate the ways that critical and creative thinking can inform, feed, tease or stimulate each other. In November 2010 we met at the home of critic Lyndon Davies; as a starting point we read an essay in which the French critic Maurice Blanchot explored the ancient Greek myth of Orpheus. In the myth, the gifted singer descends to the underworld to win back his dead love Eurydice, but fails at the very last moment to lead her to the surface. Blanchot (*The gaze of Orpheus*) finds in this material a wealth of resonances and reflections on the nature and making of art.

The range and sometimes violent strength of participants' responses could be material for another chapter; for myself, I brought a published poem of my own which used (and worked a variation on) the different but parallel myth of Persephone (*Changes of address: poems 1980–98*). Did I have anything else that used the image of a journey underground? Well, of course, the Cave Diver sequence. For the first time the poem had a frame of reference to replace that original one – or rather the focus was shifted from the publishing context (the children's collection) to the cultural context (myth). Both considerations asked *What space is this poem speaking into?* But that concept of 'space' is itself worth looking into.

The sense of an audience, and the real existence of a market in which a group of readers has been prepared by their previous reading (and by advertising) to receive on certain wavelengths, to expect certain satisfactions and to have a range of associations ready to connect with them... that is one kind of space. The form of a poem, the literal use of the space on the page is another. And here was a third, the cultural space in which whole histories of reading and responding to the matter have rendered the emptiness resonant in certain ways.

Speak the Cave Diver poems in the space prepared by the Orpheus myth, and it will resonate in certain ways.

ORPHEUS, DROWNING
Last
bubble, lithe,
mercury-skinned, my

life
in one, my lady,
now I've found her, now

I'm very small

could I curl inside

this single
breath-

sized world (say, oxygen,
say, all that life
affords),

her homuncule,

quick-
wriggling out
of the arms of gravity

her dark
companion...though
it's only her knowing of him

on her skin that lets her rise

and even could we make it,
up, to daylight, could
I live

with, could I meet
that knowledge,
daily,

in her eyes?

This is not the ending of the sequence. It is a curious
contribution which neither picks up anything in the poem
for which the reader has been prepared, nor does it step

free from the narrative of the sequence to stand by itself. The personal material which flowed in to the writing game in its origins, and possessed it, reappears here: this is the dying moment of a drowning man. The lost lady of life in it is more Persephone, again, than Eurydice, unless you find the idea of her being wedded to death in the Orpheus story too (as Rilke nearly does, in 'Orpheus. Eurydice. Hermes' where 'Being dead/fulfilled her beyond fulfillment' (*Selected poetry*, pp. 48–53). Something in it moves me, leading somewhere else, to do with any marriage or close knowing of another... but I'm content, for now, to let it slip through my fingers like that bubble, going somewhere else.

Has the Cave Diver failed? The answer might depend on your poetics. If the job of a poem is to compel a response, rhetorically, then this whole chapter is confession of its failure. Or maybe you value the reader's creative response. If so, my own urge to be that reader, to write about and from the poem is not proof of its incompleteness, but shows that its right conclusion is to make the reader, at least the one called Me, want to think on.

Meanwhile, I and I hope the readers of this piece are students of the writing process. This is offered as evidence, material towards an understanding not just of it but of how we might regard a poem, and the processes by which it gets to be itself. The subject matter is a part of it, as is the emotional resonance that makes it nag at the writer, the sense of unfinished gestalt. But the poem is more than its content; it is also the particularly-shaped space it creates in the air, on the page and in the minds of readers. Its nature unfolds differently according to various spaces into which it steps. One kind of space may be form, but there is also the space of a relationship with a reader, real or imagined – and with commercial markets. Wider, we find the distinctive spaces of a culture, pre-shaped and populated with associations, including myth.

It might be better to see the poem, then, not so much as a thing as a location, a concourse... The elements may change and go on changing; new ones are attracted, some discarded and yet – here is the practical mystery for which we are trying to find terms – the thing the poem is remains itself.

Finally, the study comes home to the point where any findings are not just literary knowledge, but those of Creative Writing specifically. That home ground is the practice of writing. Several contexts help to frame it – not determine it but offer it specific possibilities. And then the writer has to choose.

# 5   Sabyn Javeri

## A malady of the heart

Hakim Dilbar was a delicate man. There was, I thought, no other word but delicate to describe his fragility. Nearing ninety he sat cross-legged on a divan, still and calm, unfrazzled by the stifling Karachi heat. He wore a snow-white *kurta pyjama* that seemed to have been woven out of the softest of threads. His white beard, white hair and unusually pallid eyes, contrasted further by the darkness of his pupils, gave him a ghostly, ethereal appearance. If it wasn't for the red rose in his buttonhole and the strong smell of *itar* perfume that deflected from his person I would have dismissed him as an apparition.

Ami Jan pushed me down gently by the shoulders onto the silver metal stool while she sat on the chair nearby. My old ayah Halima squatted down on the floor beside the hakim sahib's throne and began her lamentations, 'Ay, Hakim Sahib, our daughter has come back to Karachi after a whole year in London-Amreeka. She went to study and her husband allowed her to go but God knows what those awful books did to her. She is not the same. Refuses to go back to her husband's home!'

Just then a rumbling voice sounded as someone cleared their throat. It was then we noticed the other man. While the elder hakim sat on the throne-like divan looking like a king observing his court, his son, a younger version of the hakim except for the lab coat and spectacles, sat hunched in a corner on a small white desk behind a large open register and a row of glass bottles filled with tiny pills and forbidding looking herbs.

'Name?' he asked, without looking up at us.

We were too taken in by the second man's presence to answer quickly. The elder hakim spoke, in a voice that seemed to have been dipped in a mixture of sugar and honey and woven like a basket of banana leaves, 'He means which one of you is the patient?'

For some reason the question made me smile, the smile spread further and a giggle came out. Where had I heard that mad people always thought it was the world around them that had become insane? Looking at Ami Jan's alarmed face as I laughed I could see that she thought I was the lunatic.

'*Nafas*,' said the elder hakim, asking for my wrist.

While the younger version pottered about with stethoscopes and charts, the Elder calmly leaned back and, taking my pulse with his thumb and forefinger, closed his eyes. When he opened them again I stared at him and asked, 'What can you see by checking my pulse that he can't with all his instruments?'

Ami Jan hushed me at my impertinence but the Elder just smiled. He had a strange smile. Only one half of his mouth lifted while the other half remained stern, the corners pointing downwards. It unnerved me to think that Papa's once full grin had been reduced to a similar smirk.

'Sometimes,' he said, scanning my face, 'the stream of our pulse carries the illness into those dark forgotten corners of our bodies where the doctor's tool cannot reach. 'Come here, Beti,' he leaned forward.

I shifted in my stool.

'*Ajijazat hai?*' he asked my mother for permission.

'Proceed,' she replied.

I swallowed, for I had heard tales of how some of these spiritual healers beat out spirits from the body, how the skin had been burned to release a trapped ghost and how they tore out your nails to remove the impurities that crawled through the opening. I shivered as I thought what would they do to someone like me?

He held my face close to his. So close that I was breathing his breath. Before I could open my mouth to protest, he flicked my eyelid inside out.

'No!' I screamed, not so much from the pain but from the unexpectedness of it all.

'Hmmm,' he mumbled. 'The secret thrives... it hides... in the dark...'

'What is it, Hakim Sahib?' Ami asked, clasping her chest.

'What do you mean what is it? They haven't even asked us why we are here,' I cried.

'It is... a Malady of the Heart,' came the hakim's verdict.

'A malady of the heart?' repeated Ami Jan.

'A malady of the heart!' echoed Halima.

'A malady of the heart,' sighed the son, closing the register with a thump as if admitting failure and putting away his charts and vials.

When we recovered from the resounding noise, Ami Jan asked, 'Surely, Hakim Sahib, with your powers there must be a cure?'

Hakim Sahib ran his fingers through his long white beard and began fingering his beads. When he spoke, his voice was low and measured. 'The heart is the main connector of the body. It is through the heart our body pumps blood, our spirit becomes purified and it is through the heart that our desires become tainted.' He looked sharply at me. 'The heart is vital but the heart is not supreme. We must remember we control it and not the other way around. The heart that does not listen becomes a danger to the self.'

As if in protest, my heart began to beat loudly against my chest. Thump, thump, thump, I felt as if I was standing naked with my breasts exposed, my nipples ripped out and only an unsightly, unruly blood-stained organ thumping itself into a slow, hollow, relentless beat.

'How much does he know?' I found myself asking for the second time that day.

The sun seemed harsh and unforgiving after the soft haze of the clinic. I blinked, squinted and rolled my eyes around, wanting to feel that my lids still worked, despite being turned inside out. As I looked sideways I noticed the alarmed look on Ami Jan's face. Suddenly I felt a softening inside my sickly heart. I was all she had, this woman. Me and God, and perhaps Halima.

We stood side by side, the three of us, silent beside each other. Three comically sad women with ill-behaved hearts that refused to listen. Me, Ami Jan and Halima – failures at the game of love. What must we look like to passers-by, I wondered? Lost wanderers searching for an address, newly discharged patients, possessed women hoping to be cured by the healer, the evil witches of Macbeth, or perhaps, just three ordinary women waiting for a rickshaw. The thought amused me and I began to laugh. But perhaps combining the laughter with an eye roll was not such a good idea for Ami Jan began to cry softly and Halima too blew her nose in her *duppatta*. But her approach to sadness was different.

'Arre that cursed driver, if only he had returned by now, we wouldn't have to wait in this horrid heat for a ride home!' Halima began to speak loudly, pulling Ami Jan under the shade of a lone tree littered with advertisements. Following them into the shade, I rested my forehead against the cool trunk and began to read the colourful advertisements aloud.

'Do you think you are going mad?' I read out. 'Think you are going to die? Get rid of the evil eye, come to Baba Ji, come today don't be shy!' I walked over to the next ad. 'Has your manhood let you down? Contact Hakim Hikmat, sole distributor of the German Mr Lover Lover Bombastic syrup.' I read slowly, my tongue feeling foreign around the Urdu script I hadn't read for eleven years. 'Are you no longer in control? Contact the Sayana Buddhu, expert in *Bangal Ka Jaadu*.' And then beneath a drawing of a heart split in two there was a number and an address. 'For the Broken-Hearted' it read. 'You break it – we mend it' read the slogan that ran all around the trunk in three tiers.

A sniffling Ami Jan trailed anxiously after me while I went round the tree reading the series of advertisements as if unwinding a string. Halima chatted away as if nothing was wrong.

'Halima, stop a taxiwallah. No use waiting around for the driver to return at an unsafe time like this,' Ami Jan said, pulling her *duppatta* closer around her face. I was unsure if she meant the city or me. Perhaps like Karachi, I too was degenerating, betrayed... and by the ones I loved.

'Alright, Begum Sahiba. As you say, but don't forget to tell off that useless driver for not showing up on time!'

'Maybe he got held up in traffic, Halima. Don't be so harsh on him all the time.'

'Arre, traffic my foot! Probably he is having potato *samosa* on the beach right now with that equally useless sweeper girl Rani! Always ready to blacken their faces, those two are. I say it is all your leniency, Begum Sahiba.'

'Oof, enough Halima, now please just go and get us a taxi,' Ami Jan replied, pressing her temples with her forefinger and thumb.

'Alright, I'll go! *Humara kya hai, hum to nokar hai.* After all I'm just a servant, what say do I have?'

'What more is left to say now, Halima,' Ami Jan nearly shouted at her.

'Fine, fine, I was just saying,' Halima replied.

Just then a yellow cab rounded the corner and I quickly flagged it down, thinking that perhaps I was of some use to them after all, when Halima barged ahead of me.

'How much to Society?'

'It is metered cab, *Bari Bi*,' replied the driver.

'Arre, old woman be your wife! I don't understand this meter-sheter. I'll give you a tenner and that's it. Take it or leave it.'

The man rolled up his window and left.

'Halima,' Ami Jan said, raising her voice to the loudest I had heard in a long time. 'Have you gone completely mad? How can you bargain at a time like this? How can you even think about it when the city is being slaughtered like a meathouse? Don't you know how unsafe the city has become since Benazir's murder?'

'Arre, Begum Sahiba, another one will be along in a short while. All is well. Just stay calm,' Halima replied a little sheepishly.

Ami Jan turned away from Halima and bumped smack into me. As we moved back, each rubbing her forehead,

Ami Jan suddenly looked me straight into the eye and said, 'Twenty-five years.'

'My age?' I asked, although I knew well by the tone of her voice that she was not joking.

'Twenty-five years I have been married to your father. Never thought of leaving. Not even the times when he left me.'

I looked away.

'He always came back. Men always do.'

'What if it's the woman who leaves?' I asked.

Now it was Ami Jan's turn to look away. I followed her gaze, trying to see what she was seeing.

All around us the city lay dug up and little hills of sand stood like miniature pyramids. Dug up roads, abandoned pipes, broken electricity poles, half-constructed buildings – some pockmarked by bullet holes – made the city look like a bombed-out war zone, yet people walked about or stood listlessly like aimless cattle, chewing toothpicks, picking their nostrils or twirling their moustache. Some twirled their waistbands like key chains. A few women stood at the junction which seemed an unofficial bus stop. A thin queue of donkey carts, cars and bikes formed behind a bus that skidded to a sudden stop, blocking the mouth of the roundabout and causing angry shouts. A man wearing a dark *shalwar* suit, stained darker by the sweat patches on his back and chest, descended and slammed the side of the bus as men quickly clambered inside, and when there was no more room left to squeeze in they climbed onto the roof, squatting like stubborn monkeys. The few women wrapped their headscarves closer to their skulls and with downcast eyes got in next to the driver. Now the man slammed the side of the

...outed, '*Jannay dey, jannay dey*, let's go, let's

...ng along with the bus as it picked up speed.

...he shouted one final time before clambering

aboard just as the bus lurched forward letting out a puff of smoke, its creaking body permanently tilted to the left and painted with colourful slogans and paintings of birds and planes.

I became so immersed in the whole rigmarole that I didn't notice Halima hailing an auto-rickshaw. The man stopped a few feet away and when Halima stubbornly refused to walk over, tapping her feet impatiently, he reversed, puffing smoke and black leather flaps each painted with an eye, right into our faces. *Bori nazar walay tera mu kala* [May you blacken your face if you put an evil eye on me], read the slogan on its back.

As we walked around to its front I noticed several more; 'Look but with Love' being the most prominent one, as it was painted in bold red lettering and a pair of eyes winking were drawn underneath. Inside on the red patent flaps a poster of the Punjabi film actress Saima had been glued, her heavy cleavage spilling out of the too-tight sari blouse nearly accosting us as we struggled to get inside the small vehicle. 'Once you come inside me you'll never want to leave!' read the sign inside the rickshaw placed strategically underneath the poster of the voluptuous actress. I could see Ami Jan's cheeks aflame as her glance fell upon the double-meaning slogan. Halima, the last one to get in, unable to read remained blissfully ignorant and chatted happily, 'Aren't you glad, Begum Sahiba, we didn't get into that *looteray* bank robber's taxi? After all, why pay so much for such a short distance anyway? Rickshaws are a far better option!'

After twenty minutes of jostling against the steel pipes of the rickshaw and the impertinent breasts of Saima, I could no longer stand the rickshaw driver's smirk in the rear-view mirror. I turned to Ami Jan but she sat so stiff and rigid that I wondered if she had turned to stone. 'Ami Jan,' I tried to speak over the roar of the rickshaw but she remained stoically still. 'Disgraceful,' she muttered when we slowed down in a traffic jam. I thought she meant the rickshaw driver but then she said, 'In our days a woman left her father's house as a bride and her husband's as a corpse.'

When I didn't reply she took my hand in hers and said, 'Think of your child.'

'You want me to stay in a loveless marriage just like you did.'

'Oh what is this love-shove? Living in London has put all these ideas in your head. In the end, my child, love boils down to nothing. It is not love that holds a marriage together but responsibility, property, children.'

*'You are my love queen, you are my heart's desire. You are my love drug, you are my…'*

Both Ami Jan and I stared at the driver as he suddenly broke into a song. He raised the volume on the radio, completely impervious to the argument behind him. I turned to Halima but she seemed suddenly subdued, tolerating the rickshaw driver's tuneless humming to the songs he was playing on the FM radio that expelled more static than music. At first I thought it was Ami Jan's harshness that had silenced her but later I figured it was the small picture of the political leader Altaf Hussein on the windshield that had got her tongue. Altaf Bhai and I had something in common. We had both been banished to London and now wished to live there in self-exile. But while I had ended there through an arranged marriage, he had escaped a jail sentence. While I was powerless and isolated back in my city, Altaf Bhai still managed to wield the power of his sword over Karachi with ruthless cynicism and a deadly following. His supporters feared no one and in turn everyone feared them. I had heard that even the Army was helpless against them and watched with averted eyes their lootings and killings against whoever they wished.

When the rickshaw, surprisingly, stopped at a red light a little boy selling newspapers flashed one in our face. 'Stop press! Benazir's murderer spotted. Killer framed in full close up! Buy your copy before it sells out. News flash, news flash, Benazir's murderer spotted. Stop press!'

Eagerly I reached out for a copy, leaving Halima to haggle the price. I turned it over searching vigorously for a name, for a face but all I saw was a silhouette of a nameless man, circled loosely. This blurry, hazy shadow was the killer. I let out a laugh, surprising not only Ami Jan and Halima but also the rickshaw driver who'd been driving with his head turned around to catch a glimpse of the paper.

'What does it say? Who killed her?' they chorused.

'This nameless blob,' I answered. As two heads bent over the page and one leaned over the divide, I pointed to a dark shadow of a man pulling a pistol so close to the back of Benazir's head that if she had turned around at that instant, she would have bumped right into him.

The rest of the journey passed in silence. When we reached home, Halima's haggling was halfhearted and she let Ami Jan pay the full fare with lacklustre grumbling as she dragged her feet inside. 'So expensive everything has become these days,' she mumbled. 'Prices are touching the sky...'

'Nothing is cheap in this country,' said the rickshaw driver, pocketing the money into the folds of his *shalwar*.

'Except human life,' added the gardener, tying up the sacks of leaves he'd raked earlier. 'They'll kill you for a mobile phone down where I live.'

As I got out of the rickshaw, the driver asked me for the paper. 'Since you have read it,' he added. I was hesitant to part with it, finding some strange perverse comfort in having a real person associated with the politician's sudden unnatural death. Life is precious, it made me think. Uncertain and short.

Before I could respond he grabbed it out of my hand, lingering for a second on my fingers. With a firm grasp on my wrist Ami Jan pulled me away from him, her eyes fixed on the picture of Altaf Hussain plastered over the rickshaw.

'Tch, tch,' we heard him mutter as he scanned the paper. 'As if the first attempt on her life hadn't been enough to teach her a lesson. No, she had to come back for seconds, this Madam did. Now look where it got her! And what good was her death to us? Complete shutdown in the country for full three days! Where is a day-wager to go? My four children and two wives starved for the three days I couldn't pick up any fares. All because of this Madam Democracy.'

The gardener came over and asked to see the paper. Satisfied, he nodded and said, 'What can you do, brother? Women don't think with their heads. They are impulsive creatures, good for running the house but not a country! After all, politics is not like shopping.'

'Right you are, brother. They don't have the brains. Not like us men you know,' said the rickshaw driver, revving up the motor, 'Women only listen to their hearts.'

In the evening we sat in my childhood bedroom, underneath a still ceiling fan waiting for the power to be restored. Riots had broken out in the city and a curfew had been imposed. We sat in the heat wondering when we would be able to step out again.

'Aye, Begum Sahiba, do you remember how hard Zara baby use to study? Barely a childhood she had, always stuck in a room with her nose buried in a book,' Halima chatted as she rubbed oil onto my scalp.

'Yes, how hard my daughter would study,' Ami Jan replied. She peeled an orange and passed it to me after rubbing it with salt and black pepper. 'From morning till noon she would be buried in books, rocking back and forth, repeating her lessons.'

Halima nodded and said, 'And for what? Just so she could get married and raise children.'

Halima didn't know it but she had just voiced something that had been piercing my insides like a rusty nail. Many lonely nights when I saw my husband absorbed in his work, I comforted myself with a magazine or a television rerun, trying to push away the thoughts that I too could have had a profession. I often wondered why they had bothered to educate me at all. Why show me a world of possibilities if you are going to move it out of my reach when I try to touch it?

'An educated girl has better prospects of a proposal from a good family,' Ami Jan replied. 'Better chances of bagging a good, educated man. Just look for yourself how cultured our Shiraz is.'

'Aye, Begum Sahiba! My husband never saw the inside of a classroom but still he was gentle-man. All of eight years that we were married, he treated me like a queen. And just for my looks he fell too, otherwise where can I read or write? It is bad for a girl to know the written word my mother use to say, it only attracts the wrath of the spirits and thick glasses! Who'd marry a girl with four eyes then?'

I knew Ami Jan was itching with irritation at the very idea of my marriage being compared to Halima's but as was her manner she simmered under a tightly sealed lid. Another slice of orange was passed to me.

'Just look at your own self, Begum Sahiba!' Halima continued, oblivious to Ami Jan's irritation. Didn't you say you went to uni-ver-city. That is a very big class, no? And look at the husband you landed. Full of bad habits our Sahib is!'

I could tell she had gone too far, for Ami Jan put away the plate in her hands and turned her whole body towards Halima and me.

'It is the good fortune of a girl to have a caring, faithful husband,' she said. 'Not everyone,' she said, waving her index finger at Halima, 'can be as lucky, but God has been kind to us. Perhaps in return for my pain He has spared my daughter. Truly it is a blessing to have a husband who is loyal.'

I knew the words would cut Ami Jan like ice but I couldn't help myself. 'And what if the wife is unfaithful?'

Ami Jan didn't talk to me for the rest of the afternoon. When we finally encountered each other in the bedroom as she was getting ready to say her prayers, I placed my hand on her arm. 'How long will you turn away from the truth Ami Jan, how long?'

'Zara,' she looked at her toes as she spoke. 'You didn't learn anything from my troubles did you? All the pain I suffered, the heartbreak, the humiliation…'

'But that was your decision to suffer. You should have left me out of it, Ami Jan. What right did you have to drag me into your mess? You chose to stay. You did it because you wanted me to hate my father, didn't you? You wanted me to hate him like you did.'

Slowly she raised her eyes to meet mine. 'I never wanted you to hate him, Zara. But I did want you to understand the meaning of loyalty.'

In that moment I thought I understood the vague isolation I had been feeling since my return. Distance may not have erased the closeness between us completely but it had buried the intimacy we had once shared. In the fading light, as Ami Jan sat on her prayer mat, framed against the window she seemed only half of the woman I used to know. I hardly recognised her, but then I hardly knew myself these days. All I knew was that I was no longer the Zara who grew up on a steady diet of fear. 'Fear Allah; he is watching you. Fear the society; people will talk. Keep your mouth shut; even the walls have ears…'

'I want to go back to London,' I said, silencing the voices in my head.

Hearing this, she folded one corner of her mat and came close to me.

'Zara, my child, your home is here now. You are lucky he let you go for a whole year when you got that scholarship. You cannot leave him now. What will people say?'

'Stop, Ami Jan. Why don't you try to understand? I

cannot live your life. I want to leave him. I want to be free. I am not the same person I was before I left Karachi. Please, I don't want to go back to my husband. '

'You can't leave, my child.'

'Ami Jan,' I tried again, 'I have felt something you never will. There is a world out there. Much larger. There is more to life than being a wife or a mother. I want to... I want...'

And then I stopped. Even to myself I sounded strange. I was battling in some sort of obscure realm, swinging between fear and desire, and to confide this awkward conflict to my mother was not possible. Perhaps I was uttering gibberish. Maybe my heart really did have a malady. How could I have thought I could be anyone other than who I really was? A good wife. A devoted Muslim. A woman.

Ami Jan took a deep breath and it seemed to me as if she had suddenly inflated. Towering over me she began reciting, '*Qul Auzu Bin Rabil Nas...* Say, I seek refuge of the Lord of all mankind; from the evil of that which whispers evil in the heart and slinks away. *Waswasay Wal Nas*, I seek refuge from those who whisper in the hearts of mankind...'

She was reciting the prayer to dispel evil spirits. I bowed my head, as I had done when I was young, for her to blow on me once she finished saying the prayer three times. In that moment I felt the distance between us bridging. I looked up hopefully but then she was gone again. Back to Him. I watched her raise her palms to her shoulders and then fold them across her chest, touch her knees with her fingertips and then fall into prostration. She seemed to be falling and rising like a clockwork toy timed to perfection, as she performed her prayers. All the time her lips kept moving. Prayer after prayer. Praise after praise for the God who was never full.

Finally she rested. Folding her legs beneath her, she raised her palms and begged His forgiveness. '*Tobah Astaghfar*,' she chanted, sitting in an upright posture. 'Forgive my sins,' she repeated thirty-three times on each finger. 'Forgive me *Ya* Allah, *Tobah Astaghfar*, God is Great, *Allah ho Akbar*, The Merciful, *Al Ghaffur*, All-knowing and Forgiving...' her words making the sinking feeling in my stomach rise up like waves in my throat.

The day before I left London, I had gone to see Aidan at his home. Number seventeen was a stoic black door in a nondescript brick building, down a narrow alley. Bland and unobtrusive, almost as if it did not want to be found. It was a small room in a small flatshare. Everything was neatly packed away. A suitcase stood in the far corner as if ready to leave. Only a sweater flung over the chair gave any sign of habitation.

'So this is where you live?' I asked

'For the time being,' he answered.

I nodded as if I understood although I didn't. I couldn't imagine sharing a house with people who were not family. I asked him how his day had been although what I really wanted to ask him was if he'd keep in touch. I searched for answers in his eyes. Will I see you again? I don't even have your number. Ask me not to go. Tell me not to go. Will you ask me not to go? Will you? Won't you? But eyes are not always easy to read. And he was a poet. Words were precious.

We sat around for a bit, talking about a poem of his that had been shortlisted for a prize. He offered me tea. I declined. Silence followed as we stared awkwardly around the bare room. When it began to sink in that this was where it all ended, all I wanted to do was leave it all behind and just say goodbye.

'I have to go now,' I said when we had talked about everything other than the future.

'Why so soon?' he asked. Not why go, I noted.

'I have to pick up my son,' I made up an excuse.

'There's still another hour till school lets out,' he whispered. 'Stay a while.'

'I have to say my prayers,' I said absently, unsure whether staying would get an answer out of him.

'Say your prayers here.'

'Here?' I asked.

'Yeah. Here. Women don't need to go to a mosque, right?'

'Right,' I repeated, wondering if he needed time to find the right words or wanted one last fuck. The last thought hurt so much, I felt like a thief who repents in the midst of a theft. What was I doing here, in this strange room with a stranger who lived in a house full of strangers? What had I become? I felt metal flood my mouth and all the tenderness I use to feel around Aidan began to feel like a self-imposed lie. In the harsh light of day, I felt simply cheap. Though the windows were shut I felt my senses flooded by the scent of jasmine. The jasmine, that came loose on Papa's bed when he came home late, the fragrance clinging to his body long after the golden goblet had been drained and the women were no longer there.

I dropped to my knees. Spreading my shawl on his faded beige carpet I began to pray without performing an ablution. I raised my palms to my shoulders, facing them outwards I chanted *Allah o Akbar* thrice. I folded my arms across my chest and recited *Surah Fatiha*. I rose up in

103

*Ruku,* kneeled over and bowed down in prostration, then dropped again, rose to my knee, chanting, praying, hoping. I don't know when it was that I began to cry and when Aidan took me in his arms. Together we rose, together we fell, our knees clunking, lacking any grace as we said the afternoon *Namaz.* I chanted in Arabic and he whispered back, 'I love you.' I kept my gaze fixed straight ahead as I continued praying through his kisses. I kept chanting the Arabic verses as he took my clothes off, kneading my breasts and pressing his nose into my neck.

I remember watching a spider crawl on the wall, a ladybug nestled in the folds of a jacket that hung on a peg as a thousand unseeing eyes looked back. I remember that my cheeks felt warm against his. *Tobah Astaghfar,* I had chanted like Ami Jan, *Tobah Astaghfar,* I had said as we kneeled on all fours. Forgive me, God, I had whispered when we stopped.

Before I left I traced my palm across his closed lids. I did not think it would be the last time I saw him.

# A malady of the mind

About three years ago, a young girl with sallow skin and huge dark circles under her eyes moved into a shadowy corner of my room. Zara took up very little space and was easy to ignore. Mostly she had her back to me and if I tried to get her to turn around she melted into a white haze. I let her be, for it was my experience that people did not like to talk till they were ready.

Then one day a bustling old woman joined her. The old woman interfered in everything I did. Her nonstop chatter filled every nook and corner of my mind till I banished her to a dark dingy drawer in the kitchen. But that did not keep her from popping up at the most unexpected times with advice I did not need. One day my mother joined the lot. 'Ami Jan?' I asked in shock for my mother lived far across the ocean in Pakistan and hated to travel. On closer inspection it turned out to be a look-alike and speak-alike of my mother. The imposter, along with the old woman, began to nag me day and night, distracting me from my daily chores to the extent that I would miss my train to work, feed my kids all sorts of unhealthy junk, rush through the housework and hardly pay any attention at work. All day I listened to their non-stop chatter. One day the chattering in my head hit the ceiling – I put sugar in the washing machine and detergent in my batter. 'That's it,' I said, silencing the three voices for good.

That night the story 'A malady of the heart' was born. It all began with the image of a spiritual healer – a *hakim sahib*. An old man in a snow-white *kurta pyjama* with a red rose in his buttonhole. The image disappeared almost as soon as it appeared and I knew somehow that in his absence was his presence. Intuition told me that the woman in the corner and the two warring old ladies held the key to rediscovering him. Reluctantly I called them back. I knew very well what I was getting into. My hectic life leaves me little time to write and often as I struggle deep into the night sacrificing sleep to write, I wonder if I should have my head examined. Why *do* I torture myself so? I could be sleeping or watching uselessly entertaining television in whatever little free time I get, yet I choose to spend it typing away on my ancient Dell. Truth is, writing is addictive. As it is with all addictions, it is mildly destructive and hugely satisfying when you are on a high. Crushing when you're down.

But coming back to the hakim, I knew I had to find out who he was and what his business is. His smile was so benign, so mysterious and eerily calm, and he spoke in such beautifully crafted sentences, a complete contrast to the coarse dialogue of the old woman, the nervous anxious whine of Ami Jan and the broody monosyllables of Zara. I knew then that a story was hidden there and that it wanted telling. So compelling was the hakim's image that I could almost feel him beside me. Instinctively I knew that a story belonged with this beginning. If only I could find the time to write it!

'Come back,' I said defeated, and the three women came flooding back. I started writing what the voices dictated and discovered that the young woman, Zara, had a secret. The irritating old woman was her ayah and the overtly pious one, her mother. They worried that the secret was eating her alive and wanted to ease her pain, yet they were afraid to learn the truth. Perhaps the hakim could help I found myself thinking. And so I went along with the three women and the rest of the story followed. I found out just a few lines before the reader that her curse was a malady of the heart. The echo that followed may well have included my voice too had I not been barred by the pen.

At a reading where I read an excerpt from this story, a renowned poet told me I had been brave to use the technique of repetition as most writers shy away from it. He laughed when I told him it was not intentional and that I was a mere scribe bullied by my characters, who insisted I take down their story exactly as they dictated. 'You care about your characters,' he told me. And it's true. For me, characters are the backbone of the story. My stories lean heavily on the character rather than the plot, sometimes at the cost of slowing down the pace of the narrative. I can't help it. I am attracted to protagonists who are the complete opposite of me. I want to find out who they are and, in time, their actions reveal their stories. For me a short story begins by exploring a characteristic, a peculiar mannerism, sometimes just a very compelling image. As the people in my stories reveal more about themselves, the story unfolds.

In that respect, a short story gives you more room to explore an aspect of a character you are interested in. It is like a first date, where you only search for what you want to know, while a novel might be like a full-on relationship.

In Malady my protagonist is a woman who is ready to stake all for love. She is brave enough to let go of her marriage, family, religion, even child – if she is allowed to. I was attracted to this facet of her personality, maybe because for me nothing comes before my children, not even writing. As they say, opposites attract. And so as I wrote, I discovered not only my protagonist's dilemmas but also my own. I realised how intrigued and at times beguiled I was by the clash between fear and desire that Zara experiences. When I got to the passage where she meets Aidan for the last time I found my fingers hovering over the keyboard, for like Zara I was hesitant to shed my own inhibitions and write something that I had been brought up to think of as taboo. In that instant I felt shame and embarrassment. But along with that came a feeling of exhilaration, a moment of letting go. Once again I found myself thinking that writing was not just a way of stretching the imagination but also of discovering one's own self. It occurred to me, as I wrote the last line, that I empathised with Zara. I understood her. And that I was on her side. And isn't that what we are all striving for in the end, to be understood? Maybe that is why writing is so appealing. Being understood is a laborious effort, yet one that we all indulge in. In fact, we fight for it. It is an act of self-preservation, an instinctive effort and one that writing makes worthwhile.

There are many characters in Malady. The story is crowded. Almost overcrowded, for I come from a culture where solitude is either the punishment of criminals or the privilege of the insane. But the unifying factor amidst them all is that they all think they are right. Each character, whether big or small, believes firmly in its own rectitude and labours to be understood. It is this self-righteousness and unshakable self-belief of the faithful that I wanted to explore. Only Zara, the protagonist, has doubts about her choice and ultimately gives in to her zealously religious mother. How she loses her certainty in the end and begins to question her intentions in the first place, is what makes her character worth exploring for me.

But as it is a short story and not a longer narrative, I am with her for only part of the journey. V. S. Pritchett describes the short story as 'something glimpsed from the corner of the eye, in passing'. Some may find that frustrating about a short story but I personally feel that it is more intriguing to sense the unsaid than for all to be revealed. I find Hemingway's analogy of fiction being like an iceberg very appealing when it comes to writing a short story. *What is above the surface should be doubled underneath by what is left out.* A short story allows you to do that. It offers an exact way of looking at things and gives you room to explore that which you want to.

In this story I wanted to get under my protagonist's skin and enter those obscure realms of fear and desire that she was feeling. Though we never learn what Zara does next, we feel her battling the uncertainty and longing that accompany her decisions. I have always been interested in the extremity of religion and the undefined boundaries of love. Perhaps it comes from having a very religious mother and a father who was an agnostic. Whatever the reason, this clash continues to fascinate me. Our protagonist is at a crossroads – she has found love, but can she break free of the beliefs that hold her back? Can she get out of her own way? Her mother's approval is very important. No matter that she has lived abroad, her resolve has been challenged back in familiar surroundings.

As I think of Zara longing for a time and place where she is free to do what she wants, I'm reminded of the despair and anguish that I and many of my fellow writers sometimes face. Most of us have a longing for that one big chunk of time where we can sit and do nothing but write. As it happens in real life, such chunks of time never appear and often we waste the little pockets of time available. Perhaps it is this frustration of the writer that manifests itself as a desire for freedom in Zara's character.

Once the story has been set, the form needs attention. In Malady, I have deliberately kept away from experimentation. I like the good old-fashioned way of starting with a strong image that intrigues the reader, then building up the protagonist and finally filling in the plot. Simplicity is best and often the most appealing narrative is that which is most straightforward. Tricking the reader only ends up making the reader feel cheated. I'm sure all of us have at some point or other shaken our head in disgust when a piece ends with, *And then I woke up*. However, presenting your work in a way that compels the reader to think, to put in knots s/he must untie and to add twists and turns that leave one gasping and edging for more, is always welcome. Though not always easily achievable…

I try not pay attention to the structure or style while I'm writing as I think editing or even questioning your work hampers creativity. The first draft is almost a free-flow stream of consciousness. It is when I have said everything I wanted to that I go back and edit. But not before some time has passed. First I let it stew in my mind, in an almost obsessive manner. Just like after walking out of an argument – one wished to have said this or that, stayed quiet at this point and lashed out at another – I ponder the possibilities. One might find it funny that I am comparing writing to an argument and perhaps it is a wrong analogy. Battle is more like it!

Usually, when I go back to it after a few weeks, the one question that always haunts me is, *did I really need to say that in so many words?* Here I like to unleash my inner editor, the vicious ten-headed monster who questions every word, every comma on every line. And as I do so, the form tightens. I go along the page crossing out the 'telling' – all those scenes and dialogues which report what the character is feeling, replacing it with 'showing'. I try and see it visually as if it was a film where the actors must act out how they are feeling rather than speak out their thoughts. And then, after putting it away for another week or so, I pull out the final test. I ask myself that if the story was a drop of water and I lifted up the page, would it slide right off the edge or would it stall, blocked this way and that, unable to flow naturally? Some sort of author antennae or creative instinct akin to the sixth sense is needed to gauge the answer. And I ask myself, can it be summed up in one line? Can the gist of the story be felt immediately, is the message clear, the storyline uncluttered? If yes, it is time to lock it up again.

I then enjoy the freedom till once again the characters begin to haunt me and I am compelled to open the drawer and read the story aloud. If it reads like I could not possibly have written it – then it's ready. Ready to go out in the big bad world and find itself a home. And that's where it all ends. Only to start all over again when a new idea germinates in the mind...

But that is the thrill and beauty of a short story. Its compelling nature, its creative expression. The short story is that rare form of literature that follows just one rule, which is that there is no rule. It is fluid like water, can flow in any direction or be stagnant. It is a fleeting feeling, a glimpse, a moment in time. It is not meant to satisfy but to whet your appetite for more good writing, arouse your curiosity about a culture, make you envious of a character or simply leave you with a sharp sense of relief – and anticipation.

# 6   Colm Breathnach

*The pulse of language*

DÁN '300' (IS A SEACHT)

Tógann an file

    Bád,
    an léitheoir
    a chuireann an criú inti
    a chuireann í ag seoladh;

    Sáipéal,
    is is é an léitheoir
    a chuireann an cór ann
    a líonann é le ceol;

    nó
    Spás,
    a fheistítear le troscán
    go ndéantar seomra do.

Tógann an file
leathanach dubh
is lena pheann
súnn do an dúch
go n-aimsíonn an dán
ina lár.

Tógann an léitheoir
Dán.

Bíonn
an file
gan a bheith ar fáil.


POEM '300' (AND SEVEN)

The poet builds

   a Boat,
   the reader
   provides the crew
   that sets it sailing;

   a Chapel,
   and it's the reader
   puts the choir in it
   that fills it with music;

   or
   a Space,
   that gets fitted out with furniture
   and becomes a room.

The poet
takes a black page
and with his pen
absorbs the ink
and discovers the poem

in its centre.

The reader builds
a Poem.

The poet
is wont
to be unavailable.

## OÍCHE MHAITH, A BHASTAIRD
*do m'athair*

Ar an mBuailtín
os cionn shiopa Sheáinín na mBánach,
a bhíodh na hoícheanta againne
agus thagadh scata do mhuintir na háite
is dos na 'laethanta breátha'
thar n-ais i ndiaidh am dúnta
i dtigh tábhairne Dhónaill Uí Chatháin.

Is bhímísne, páistí, inár leapacha ar fionraí,
suan na súl oscailte orainn sa tseomra codlata
ag feitheamh le monabhar bog an chomhluadair
ag déanamh orainn an staighre aníos.

Thosnaítí ansan le tamall comhrá
scéalta á n-aithris is corrsá grinn,
tú fhéin i d'fhear tí támáilte
ach an Beamish ag tabhairt do ghlóir chugat
nó go n-iarrtá ar dhuine éigin amhrán a rá.

An curfá dá chasadh ages gach éinne,
an siosa agus an barr dá bhaint do bhuidéal.

Is nuair a bhíodh an oíche thart
chloisimís na daoine is iad ag imeacht,
thíos ar an tsráid i moch na maidine
an ceiliúradh ag duine acu, 'Oíche mhaith, a bhastaird',
in ard a chinn ar shráid an Bhuailtín.

Is é mo lom
ná rabhas fásta suas in am,
sara bhfuairis bás,
le go mbeinn i láthair
ag oíche a reáchtáilis
os cionn shiopa Sheáinín
ar an mBuailtín.

Is nuair a bheadh an oíche thart
agus an chuideachta ag imeacht
thabharfainn fhéin faoi mo lóistínse mar aon leo
i mBaile Eaglaise nó sna Gorta Dubha
ach sara n-imeoinn chasfainn chugat
le do ndéarfainn, 'Oíche mhaith, a bhastaird',
go ceanúil meisciúil leat.


GOOD NIGHT, YA BASTARD
*to my father*

In Ballyferriter on holidays
we stayed above Seáinín na mBánach's shop
and some nights
a crowd of locals
and summer visitors
would return after closing time
in Daniel Keane's pub.

We, the children, lying in suspense
feigning sleep in our beds
waiting for the soft murmur of the company
making its way up the stairs.

Things would start with a bit of a chat,
stories being told, fun being poked,
you acting as shy host
'til the Beamish gave you voice
and you called for a song.

Everyone joining in the chorus,
the hiss as another bottle is opened.

And when the revelling was over
we'd hear the people going,
down on the road in the early morning
someone shouts, 'Good night, ya bastard',
in the full of his voice on the village street.

My sorest wish
to have grown up in time,
before you died,
so I could come
to a night you organised
over Seáinín's shop
in Ballyferriter.

And when the night was over
and the company were going
I would head for my own lodgings too
in *Baile Eaglaise* or the *Gorta Dubha*.
Before I left I would turn to you
and say 'Good night, ya bastard',
fondly, tipsily.

## DÁ GCÍFEÁ Í TAR ÉIS FÍON A DH'ÓL...
*do Mhicheál agus Michelle*

Dá gcífeá í tar éis fíon a dh'ól,
an cineál craorag sin ón tSile a mhiceo,
í ag pramsáil romham tríd an gceantar gnó
i lár na hoíche agus loinnir ina snó
mar nár fhágamar an tábhairne 'dtína ceathrú chun a dó.
Á, dá gcífeá í tar éis fíon a dh'ól.

Dá gcífeá í tar éis fíon a dh'ól,
cineál na Gearmáine ar a dtugaid Hoch,
a lámha amhail éin bhána ag gabháil gach treo
is a glór ag breith bua ar challán an tsló
i gcaifé súgánach san ardtráthnón'.
Ó, dá gcífeá í tar éis fíon a dh'ól.

Dá gcífeá í tar éis fíon a dh'ól,
sútha talún faoi uachtar agus Beaujolais Nouveau
ag cóisir ghairdín i dtosach an fhómhair
a rothar le hais an gheata is é ag brionglóid
faoin mbóthar abhaile is an ghrian ag dul fó.
Á, dá gcífeá í tar éis fíon a dh'ól.

Dá gcífeá í tar éis fíon a dh'ól,
bán ón nDomhan Úr, ó fhíonghoirt Chalafóirn',
i lár halla ag hapáil tríd an nGoirtín Eornan
ina bróga gorma svaeide nua.
Dá gcífeá í mar a chímse í tar éis fíon a dh'ól...

## IF YOU COULD SEE HER AFTER DRINKING WINE...
*to Micheál and Michelle*

If you could see her after drinking wine,
Wine from Chile of the berry-red kind
Prancing ahead of me in the middle of the night
Through the business district with her face alight
Having left the pub late and a little tight.
Ah, if you could see her after drinking wine.

If you could see her after drinking wine.
Wine called Hoch from Germany's Rhine
Her hands like birds fluttering in flight
In a sugawn café when the day is high
Her voice louder than the crowd's by just a mite.
Oh, if you could see her after drinking wine.

If you could see her after drinking wine,
Beaujolais Nouveau, strawberries and cream
At a garden party under autumn's gleam
Her bike by the gate lost in a dream
Of the road home as the sun goes to sleep.
Ah, if you could see her after drinking wine.

If you could see her after drinking wine.
Wine from California's grape-fields fresh and new
Hopping through the Stack-of-Barley a bit askew
In her oh so new blue suede shoes.
If you could see her, as I see her, after drinking wine.

## AN LEABHAR ÁRSA

Tóg an leabhar ársa seo
go bhfuil an clúdach leathair air ag dul i léithe,
go bhfuil na ciumhaiseanna ar na leathanaigh ann ar
scéitheadh
agus an dúch orthu, leis, ag tréigean.
Tóg an leabhar ársa seo agus léigh é.

Léigh pé méid do is áil nó is féidir leat.
Faigh peann is téigh thar aon litreacha ann atá ag éag.
Scrios amach aon fhocail atá míshoiléir
agus breac isteach focail de do chuid fhéin.

Mar chlabhsúr
cuir focail eile
as a dheireadh,
scrígh aon ní is áin leat.
Fút féin atá go hiomlán,
anois.

Dein an méid seo céim ar chéim
agus chífir de réir a chéile
liathadh an chlúdaigh
scéitheadh na gciumhaiseanna
agus tréigean an dúigh
ag dul ar gcúl
chífir an ghnáthmhíorúilt ag tarlúint,
don leabhar ársa déanfar tráchtas úr.

## THE ANCIENT BOOK

Take this ancient book
with its leather cover moulding
and the crumbling edges of its pages
and the ink on them becoming faint.
Take this ancient book and read it.

Read as much as you want or as you can.
Take a pen and go over any letters there that are fading.
Delete any words that are indistinct
and insert words of your own.

Finally
add other words
at the end,
write anything you want,
it is entirely up to you
now.

Do all this step by step
and you will see by degrees
the mould on the cover
the crumbling of the margins
and the fading of the ink
reversed
you will see the usual miracle taking place,
the ancient book become a fresh treatise.

# Language itself

All creative writing starts with language, not with ideas, plot outlines, rhythms or literary theories but simply with language itself, with words and the desire to use words in a particular way. Anyone who hasn't yet written anything, but says 'I have a great idea for a novel' must surely have initially, at some point prior to that, felt that desire, that little spark of conception created perhaps by the way words can at times rub against each other unexpectedly in the mind. It is this that brings on the 'great idea'. I remember as a child, before I had started school, telling my mother stories. These were stories I made up myself, probably based on the tales she told me or the children's storybooks she had read to me. This was, of course, child's play. But it grew out of a play-instinct that was more a desire to articulate a world or a scene imagined in the mind rather than a desire to impart a narrative. My stories didn't begin with 'Once upon a time there was...' but *in medias res* with 'A leprechaun sits under a tree...'. Later this instinct in me would became poetry. This desire to fit words, language, to my way of thinking, or more urgently, my way of feeling. The narrative follows on from that, of course, whether in poetry or prose, as we begin to tell our story, to relate to ourselves and to relate ourselves to others.

For me, from the start, writing has always been, and still is, quite literally, a question of language. All bilingual writers, of course, have to address the question of which language they will write in. This may be a question of the moment, as in which language will I use for this current piece or it may be, as I suspect, the more common question of which language will I use as a writer. There are, of course, many writers who write in more than one language. It may not be the case, though, that their readership always follows them across the language divide. I can think of two poets, for instance, who have produced substantial bodies of work in both Irish and English and, though I have read their Irish poetry, I am almost totally unfamiliar with their work in English. So the question of which language one writes in can also be about the audience the writer seeks to address or the audience the writer most wants to write for.

I was raised speaking two languages. All of my education was through the Irish language but, apart from that, I used English mostly in the home and almost exclusively outside of the home. When I began to write, I wrote in English. In my late teens, however, I began more and more to write in Irish and I have written in Irish exclusively since. The decisions and the choices we make shape the personality and our personalities influence our decisions and choices.

I was fortunate to be raised with two languages but the time came, as it had to come, when I was in danger of falling between the two languages as far as my poetry was concerned. I was between two practices. I had two names for everything and accordingly I had two ways of describing the world. But poetry is not description. It is a desire that can't be refused, a need, a sharp necessity and in the end, for my part, I found I could only attend to that necessity through the medium of one of those languages.

It is argued frequently that recourse should not be had to anything in the life of the author outside of the work in order to interpret any particular piece. The case of the bilingual writer, however, throws up an interesting phenomenon that is worth taking into account and that is why I referred to my own background here. In so far as what I wrote in the two languages was not, and never could be, the same, we can discern one of the things that inspires the author or that makes an author of the author, as you might say, and that thing is the specific reaction that occurs between the author and the language. It is to a certain extent, in my view, as simple as that. There is, between the individual and the language, some particular relationship that contributes to creating the work. Every language is an organic process. Neither a dictionary nor a grammar, but a network of connotations, constructs, connections, concurrences and combinations each of which changes constantly with use. Add to that, matters as fundamental as the unique syntax of the language and the sounds of the language and there you have that thing which is the medium the writer must employ. The author composes a work full of significance, within the two meanings of that word, through the use he makes of all those aspects of the language and, in my case, I came to realise I was more successful in achieving that in Irish than in English. It is no harm to emphasise this point, that the author does this consciously for the most part and that is why, frequently, bilingual writers must of necessity make a choice between the two languages. I think something in my personality shaped this choice and the choice shaped my personality in turn.

As regards the sounds of a language, the actual 'music' of the words, the poet Liam Ó Muirthile (*A new view of the Irish language*, p. 147) emphasises the importance these hold for poetry and in particular for poetry in the Irish language:

Language carries meaningfulness beyond semantics, perhaps into some area of the collective unconscious... The sounds of Irish poetry move us in mysterious ways. The language itself has a strange hold on us, beyond reasonableness. It is possible to view the vast panoply of Irish poetry, for example, as a language with an unwritten notation, the music of itself. One of the tasks in dealing with it is to absorb it aurally as much as to read it.

It was in this quality of the Irish tradition, in the implicit condition that expression be a function not only of the superficial meaning but also of underlying rhythms and half-suggested echoes that I discovered my voice. The key to composing the kind of poetry that I wanted to write was contained in the musicality of the language. The poetic urge is in Irish referred to as *cuisle na héigse*, or the poetic vein or pulse, thus poetry is the pulse of language, the beat in the blood, the resonating rhythm. I began, not so much to capture or to harness the rhythms and cadences of the traditional songs that I heard my mother and friends of my parents sing, as to let them loose in my poetry, to let them swirl through and around the images I created and the moments of memory I wished to recall, the emotions I tried to relay. In an essay on modern poetry in Irish, the poet Louis de Paor remarks on this approach in my early work: 'many of the poems in [the earlier work] are as much about the reflexive pleasure of language itself and its legitimate indulgence as they are about the apparent subject matter' (*The Cambridge history of Irish literature*, vol II, p. 350).

Young children in school in Ireland very often learn the basic steps that will carry them through most simple Irish traditional pattern dances – one two three, one two three, one two three four five six seven, one two three and one two three. Sometimes, when I begin to write a poem, it is a little bit like learning a new dance. A phrase or a line, or a cluster of words, begins to chime in the mind. Once you have the basic steps and you listen to what the words are telling you, you can begin to follow the dance, to write out the poem so that the burden of what you are saying moves to the accompaniment of the score that the words themselves advance. This is the starting point and the basis, in my case, for my poetic voice.

There is, of course, more to it than that, but establishing one's own ground, one's own approach to melody, as it were, allows the writer to begin to cultivate the use of the apparatus provided by the language in a distinctive way, and so eventually to give a signature performance. It may be that in another poet, or as regards poetry written in another language, the emphasis will lie on a different aspect of the language rather than that which I have highlighted. But it will always involve a particular relationship between the writer and language or the poet and language.

Every language embodies, in some way, a particular world view, if only, for instance, in the way that it classifies objects, divides time into grammatical tenses or outlines different relationships through its use of separate prepositions. All the speakers of a particular language are referred to as a language community, and the language those speakers share is called a community language. Of course, as a sign that the writer and the reader belong to the one community we can point to the fact that they share the one language. The language that a writer uses in his work is at one and the same time an artistic medium and a means of communication for a language community.

That ever-changing, constantly developing network of connotations, constructs, connections, etc. that I outlined above, serves as a link between two minds, the mind of the writer and the mind of the reader, and those three agents, the mind of the writer as revealed in the work, the language as presented in the work and the mind of the reader as it is engaged by the work together bring the work to life. The artifice of the artist we call a writer and the participatory nature of the relationship between the writer and reader depend on the writer's use of language. The poet for his part, at one and the same time, affirms and alters the language in so far as the poem will depend for its meaning on the proper use of aspects of the language network and will also most probably depend for its effect on some novel, or at least striking, use of connotation, construction or connection. The writer's use of language will, of course of necessity, despite any novelty, have to be capable of being followed by the reader in order for the work to be recognised as art. This continuously altering medium where the meaning of a word and the echoes it evokes can change depending on the context is embodied in what we call tradition. The individual writer again, at one and the same time, draws from and contributes to that tradition in his writing.

As well as realising that the musical nature of the Irish tradition offered me the opportunity to explore that aspect of my poetic voice, to exploit that (im)pulse within me, I later realised that I imagined I was better able to manipulate the whole network of connections and constructs associated with the Irish language than I was in the case of English and also that I felt closer poetically to my contemporaries in Irish and to my imagined Irish language readers than to any possible local subset of English language writers or audience. It was not only a question of musicality, but also a matter of being more at home with the echoes I could evoke in one language than I was in the other, with the tap my poetic dancing feet made in one language rather than the other. I know, simply from of my knowledge of both languages, that, as regards many of the poems I have written in Irish, or most probably every poem I have written in Irish, in fact, that I could never have written them in English. This is despite the fact that I am fluent in English and that I carry on quite a lot of my daily life through the medium of English.

I have, however, managed to provide quite passable translations into English of a good many of my poems after they are written. This only serves once again to highlight the primacy of language, rather than material, in poetry and, I believe, in creative writing in general. The case of the bilingual writer illustrates the importance of the relationship of the writer to language. We don't always read particular writers just to hear what they have to say but rather to hear how they say it. We often return to certain writers or seek out other works of theirs not because of what they said but because of their manner of saying things in general, not for the story but because of the way the story is told.

In the poem '**Dán '300' (is a Seacht)**' ('Poem '300' (and seven)'), I addressed the relationship between the poet and the reader (*'Dánta' agus dánta eile* p. 5). In a sense, the poet and the reader share the space that is the poem. The poet creates the space through his use of language. The reader fits out the space according to his understanding of what the poet is saying. The poet of course is both present and absent during the reader's reading of the poem. The image of the poet discovering the poem in a page covered with black ink is based on my idea of the way a sculptor discovers the statue in block of stone and also hints at the way the poem emerges almost by itself or is revealed by degrees under the strokes of the pen on the page.

The poem **'Oíche Mhaith, a Bhastaird'** ('Good night, ya bastard') appears in the collection *An Fear Marbh*. My father died when I was seventeen years old. I was in my first year at university. Before he died my father became invalided and housebound. My mother was working, so it fell to me very often to stay at home and take care of him during the last few months of his life. Being father and son we had disagreed and argued quite a lot when I was younger, but we grew closer during this period. Years later I began to write some poems in memory of my father. I wrote a short sequence which was published in my second collection, but it wasn't until the time that the seventeenth anniversary of his death was approaching and I realised that shortly I would be alive longer without my father than I had been with him in my life, that I was moved to commemorate him more fully. The collection *An Fear Marbh* was the result. It is a collection of poems to my father. The title is a reference to *Inis Tuaiscirt*, the most northerly of the Blasket Islands that lie off the coast of County Kerry in the west of Ireland. From the mainland, this island looks like a man stretched out on his back and is therefore often called *An Fear Marbh* ('The Dead Man'), particularly by outsiders. In the late sixties and the seventies, the family spent summer holidays in that area of west Kerry, as it is a *Gaeltacht*, an area where the population is predominantly Irish-speaking and my parents were anxious for their children to hear the language being used as an everyday language. Some of the holiday-makers and certain locals became close friends over the years and so every year there would be nights when they might meet in the local pubs and continue the party in someone's house thereafter. Because I have happy memories of my father from those days of our holidays, when I was writing the collection I found myself recreating how one of those nights might have been from the point of view of a child listening to the adults partying.

This poem gives a practical illustration of the effect of the choice to write in Irish, I think. The background of the poem is one familiar to Irish speakers. Non-native speakers of Irish very often spend holidays in *Gaeltacht* areas in order to perfect their command of the language. They stay in the houses of locals, native speakers, or rent accommodation from them and of course they socialise together very often as well. I mention particular people and places and I use some local slang that would have been well known to members of the Irish-speaking community with whom I grew up. If I had tried to write this poem in English, the audience I would be addressing, though Irish, would have been unfamiliar for the most part with the context. The regret in the poem, which is realised through the idea of the son not having taken his place as an adult, before the death of the father, in a particular community deliberately cultivated by the father, has to do with a very definite cultural context. The loss of the father encompasses, in that way, the loss of a continuity that is wider than simply the familial relationship. Thus I am

131

sure it would have been impossible to write this poem in English. This is not to say that it cannot be translated into English, but simply that the initial impulse of the poem, as opposed to the poem itself, belongs to a context that is wholly foreign to English.

From that initial impulse the poem was worked out, or worked itself out, under the strong influence of sound patterns, with echoes of traditional metres, that carried the argument through to the end. The opening and middle parts of the poem contain strong long a (á) vowels which modulate to a more understated long u (ú) rhyme at the end. Had I tried to write the poem in English I would have had to travel by different paths to reach the same destination. At times then, it can be almost as if the two languages describe the same life but relate it in radically different ways.

I wrote '**Dá gCífeá í Tar Éis Fíon a dh'Ól...**' ('If you could see her after drinking wine...') after my wife and I had been out for dinner with friends. I had known both Micheál and Michelle separately before they met each other and were married and in all the time I knew her I had never known Michelle to drink. That night, however, she had wine with her meal. When I remarked that I had never seen her drinking, Micheál jokingly said, 'You should see her after drinking wine'. The poem (*Chiaroscuro*, p. 1) grew out of that line.

One of the pleasures of writing is having an opportunity to write a poem for friends arising out of a shared occasion of this kind. The poem revolves partly around real events we were present at but primarily around imagined instances that may be appropriate to the wines listed. Apart from one or two references, there isn't anything particularly Irish about the poem nor does it contain anything that belongs specifically to the Irish tradition. The word 'sugawn' (from the Irish *súgán*) means a straw rope or cord and in the poem is used in reference to the type of chairs with seats made with woven cord often found in small cafés. The 'Stack-of-Barley' is a traditional dance. Apart from these cultural references, the poem could relate more or less to any place. Despite that, the poem in Irish uses one end rhyme throughout – all the lines end in a long o sound (ó). This is something I would never have attempted in English and is something that probably would not have worked even if I had written the poem that way in English. It is, however, something that adds to the enjoyment of the poem in Irish. The long o rhymes are achieved in some cases by the use of dialect pronunciations and oblique forms of words. The wine Beaujolais Nouveau may not be the most fashionable of wines, and it certainly presented a French friend of mine who was translating the poem into French with an almost existential question as to whether it should even be mentioned in poetry, but from my point of view it offered a convenient long o sound at the end of a line.

The poem **'An Leabhar Ársa'** ('The ancient book') is a recent poem (*'Dánta' agus dánta eile*, p. 11). It arose from something I misheard one day on the radio. I thought I heard someone refer to an ancient book. I realised later they weren't talking about a book, be it ancient or otherwise, but the idea of the ancient book stayed with me all day and I found myself writing the poem without any real idea of where it was going or what it referred to. The second

133

line – *go bhfuil an clúdach leathair air ag dul i léithe* ('with its leather cover moulding') – contains a direct reference to a line from a seventeenth-century poem, 'D'aithle na bhFileadh', by Dáibhí Ó Bruadair. In it the poet laments the disregard among the young of his day for native learning and cites the condition in which once-treasured books are left – *a leabhair ag tuitim i leimhe's i léithe i gcúil* ('their books... lie mouldering, covered with dust', *Duanaire Dháibhidh Uí Bhruadair* part III, p. 4). This then is the starting point of the poem, an ancient book seemingly discarded or 'unheeded' as John Mac Erlean interpolates in his translation of the Ó Bruadair poem.

When I imagined the ancient book I was thinking of a leather-bound manuscript. The practice among patrons of having scribes copy books containing poems and stories in Irish by hand continued well into the nineteenth century. Much of the Irish literature we have today from the middle ages and later periods came down to us in this way. I suppose it was this kind of book that I had in mind as I wrote. Often it happened that a scribe may not have understood older material exactly and he would insert his own words in the text. In my poem, I imagine the book as having faded in parts and needing to have the words rewritten or even replaced with new words. In this way I see the book being renewed. It is at this point that the poem turns. I think it was here that I realised where I was going with the poem or, where the poem was taking me, if you like. By degrees the instructions become what might be termed more positive – 'insert words of your own' and 'write anything you want' and 'Finally/add other words'. In the final part of the poem where the decay is reversed in the Irish I have reversed the word order of the first part so the sound pattern of long u (ú) sounds followed by long e (é) sounds in the first part becomes long e sounds followed by long u sounds in the final part, so that the music matches the meaning.

I see this poem as an enactment of the way not only Irish literature has been handed on through the generations but of the way any body of knowledge or lore or any tradition or even family history is passed on. Tradition, just like a language, is an organic construct that changes over time as it is added to and as material gets discarded or forgotten. I hope my poem views this process in an optimistic manner. Any tradition needs to be re-invented, renewed or even re-imagined or reformulated if it is to be of any benefit to those who rely on it. Those who belong to the tradition or to whom the tradition belongs need to be able to manipulate it in their turn, otherwise it ends up becoming a dead decaying thing, a mouldering, impenetrable dusty tome.


I have tried, with the aid of the four poems I have presented here, to illustrate to some extent my approach to writing and my views on what is actually taking place when we write poetry and perhaps when we read poetry.

What makes us poets is that we can't simply let life happen around us without commentating on it. We are just like the young boy playing football alone in his back garden and commentating on the action at the same time. We are constantly recreating events, emotions and celebrating moments from our lives in words even as they happen. We present ourselves through language or the language presents itself through us. The poem, that point of reaction between the inner self and the language of the community is the site where the alchemy occurs. For me this could only be brought about in the Irish language. That it was achieved is recognised by the critic Máirín Nic Eoin (*Filíocht Chomhaimseartha na Gaeilge*, p. 233, excerpt translated from Irish by the present author):

> The language of his poetry is distinctive – the idiom he uses is dialectal without being parochial, native without being aphoristically old-fashioned. His is a rich urban speech deeply rooted in the literary tradition of the Irish language but always in tune with the complexities of contemporary life.... Suitability matters and precision is valued, particularly in light of the realisation that 'our minds only touch fingertips/even when at our most lucid' ('Amhras' ['Doubt'] *Scáthach* p. 102)

All writers create their own precious metal in their own way, of course, but whether that initially involves making a choice between languages or a decision to use a particular language in certain circumstances or a choice between idioms or registers or dialects in a single language or doesn't involve any conscious determination one way or the other, the poet always has to start with language. Ideas, propositions or arguments don't make poems. How language is used to present ideas or propositions, or emotions etc., or to create them in words is what determines whether or not the reaction has been successful.

The question has been asked, why would someone who has had the benefit of the 'silver spoon' of the English language in their mouth, a world language with such an extensive tradition, turn to a lesser-spoken language like Irish which, though it has a literary history that stretches back to the early eighth century and beyond, is nonetheless a minority language in a very straitened state that offers few opportunities for reaching a wide audience (Ní Dhuibhne, 'Why would anyone write in Irish?'). The simple answer to this question is, of course, that it is very hard to articulate your own voice when you do have a silver spoon in your mouth. My inclination to write in Irish was, in many ways, more a turning towards Irish rather than a rejection of English. The English I spoke was divorced in my mind from the type of English I felt I needed to use in my writing. I found myself either writing honest poems where my voice may have been genuine but limited in range, or poems that verged on a pastiche of the style of poem that I wanted to write. At the same time the voice that emerged in the poems I was writing in Irish sounded authentic. The persona that began to reveal itself felt comfortable clothed in the syntax of the language. There was no striving for effect, because in this particular dance the language itself did the leading.

And this simple fact, this idea that the individual writer needs to find his own voice even if that means choosing one language over another when that choice is available, this idea that the poet has to ensure that the language expresses itself through him, rather than simply using language, is what I see as central to the art of the poet. Poets are the guardians of the pulse of language, that constant flow that keeps our words on their toes, and it is their function to keep language exercised and limber. When you let language lead rather than trying to constrict its movement, it frees the language and allows it to express itself in new ways through you, through your individual voice. It is this that identifies the individual, gives the individual identity within the tradition. And it is this that makes writing creative and original.

# 7  Emily Raboteau

*Rapture*

Now that the days shuffle into each other like a deck of cards I can't remember which of the eight classes was the one where we learned about the Rapture. But I can remember the name of the woman who first told us about it – Bernadette – because it was on our short list of girl names. As it turned out I gave birth to a boy and we named him Clay.

Bernadette was a willowy white woman with long hair, a long face and a long torso. She was a modern dance teacher and spoke about being thrown off the dance by her new centre of balance. I envied her ankles, which remained slender as pilsner glasses, deep into the third trimester. Even though her due date fell a week before mine, she looked a lot less pregnant. Her posture was perfect. She wore her new belly like an accessory. I, on the other hand, was not a graceful pregnant woman. I was as big as America. You name it, I had it: varicose veins, oedema, zits, nausea, heartburn, haemorrhoids, gas, bovine brain... The load was almost too much to bear.

My legs felt like they'd been torn off and then rejoined the wrong way in the sockets of my child-bearing hips. My swollen feet no longer fitted into my shoes. Plus, I was afflicted by something called 'round ligament pain,' which was far too anodyne a description for the stabbing sensation it produced in my groin when I walked. I had new sympathy for the little mermaid in the fairy tale who, having traded her fish tail for love, felt on her brand new legs that she was stepping on knives. I'd never felt so uncomfortable in my thirty-five years. I'd never felt so powerful.

'So when are you due?' Bernadette asked. An ice-breaking question, so it was probably the first or second birthing class. It was probably the break and we were probably standing with our husbands by the snack table, munching on rice crackers, wasabi peanuts or carrot sticks dipped in hummus. And we were probably smiling.

'May 21,' answered my husband, Anthony. He patted my navel, possessively. He was always doing that then, as if to assure himself the pregnancy was real. I stopped myself from patting his middle in return, something I liked to do in bed at night to reassure myself that he was real too, that we were indeed a family. Over those nine months we gained the exact same amount of weight at the exact same rate. There was a term for that too – Couvade syndrome – though to my husband it was just an embarrassing spare tyre he masked by leaving his shirt untucked. Secretly, I preferred him this way, a little bit fat. That's who Anthony was – substantial and solid but soft. He was fat when I first met him. Then he got successful, married me and went on a diet, though not necessarily in that order. Before he knocked me up and started growing back alongside me he was a big man masquerading in a thin man's body.

'May 21?' Bernadette's husband gave Bernadette a meaningful look. It was half pointed and half playful and he had to raise his eyes to deliver it because she was taller by half a head. I can't remember his name. Dave or Nick or something equally forgettable. He was a sad-sack, a balding tax accountant who favoured plaid and clearly adored her. His face was perpetually anxious, except for the time he got over-excited while watching the orgasmic birth video and Bernadette had to smack his shoulder to get rid of his grin. They'd met on an online dating site. So had everyone else in the class aside from the couple with matching haircuts who met in a college a cappella group, the lesbians who worked together at the botanical garden in the Bronx, and Anthony and me. We liked to think we had the most romantic story of all.

By national, if not New York City, standards we were most of us old to be having our first children. Middle age was around the corner. Some of us were recovering from the desperation and fear that we couldn't conceive by choosing to birth naturally, to be present for every sensation. How else, apart from her ticking clock, could Bernadette's husband have pulled her off?

'Don't tell them,' she warned him.

'Don't tell us what?' Anthony asked.

'Nothing,' said Bernadette.

'But now you have to tell us,' I said.

'It's stupid,' said Bernadette.

'What's stupid?' Anthony pushed, taking my hand. 'Let us be the judge.'

Bernadette was annoyed. 'You tell them,' she ordered Nick or Dave.

'I'm sorry,' he said, looking at his shoes. 'I shouldn't have brought it up.'

'But you did. You did bring it up,' Bernadette spat.

'Okay,' he said.

There came an awkward silence which Bernadette finally broke. 'Your due date – May 21, 2011? It's supposed to be the second coming,' she said.

'According to those evangelical yoyos,' her husband apologised, adjusting his glasses.

'That's awesome,' said Anthony, somewhat defensively. He refused to entertain bad omens as far as the baby was concerned. But also, because he loved comic books and horror movies and all characters with special powers, it appealed to his particular blend of optimism and drama to imagine our kid might be the saviour.

'If you think the end of the world is awesome,' said Bernadette with a weird hostility. She was probably just angry at her husband for bringing up the Rapture in the first place, but Anthony and I automatically stiffened at her tone. As usual when we were the only brown people in the room, we were quick to guard ourselves against subtle and not so subtle slights. Who was she to tell us there was something wrong with our kid's birthday when he wasn't even born yet? Hadn't the guy who predicted May 21 as the end of days already gotten it wrong twice before? And didn't we already learn in the birthing class that our due dates were relatively arbitrary? Our baby was just as likely to arrive some other day.

The birth instructor would have clapped her hands to signal the end of the break right about then. She was an earth mother type who'd failed to make it in musical theatre but still pulled out her bright stage voice and jazz hands to discuss labour. I loved her for her naked enthusiasm. It was getting harder and harder to find people who weren't sarcastic. 'When your contractions bring you to the transition stage, do a dance. Don't lose faith, people! Your baby's on the way. Remind yourself you're about to meet the love of your life.'

Maybe she showed us a homebirth video at that point, or had us look at a cervical diagram in the workbook, the stages of dilation configured in a bull's eye of concentric circles, or maybe she coached us to breathe through a contraction while holding ice cubes in our palms. She might also have demonstrated with her model pelvis and plastic doll where the baby's head would sit right before it was time to push. Anthony may have taken notes while I felt the baby quickening or hiccuping inside me. I'm thinking this couldn't have been the class where she told us how to deliver on our own in the unlikely event of an emergency. That probably came later.

Anthony and I first met at John F. Kennedy Airport when I flew in from my long sojourn in Brazil, finally exhausted from the effort of trying to find myself. There he was, as planned, standing in the arrivals hall with the cluster of chauffeurs, wearing a cheap dark suit from Big and Tall and holding a placard with a question mark on it. At that time I was a drug mule and he was living in Queens a mile away from the airport in his mother's basement. She charged him a little rent which he earned from time to time by running errands, like this pickup, for an unsavoury childhood friend.

I was a much bigger loser than Anthony. He just couldn't see it. I'd had my share of addictions, lovers, heartache and STDs, and I was broke. I was smuggling five kilos of cocaine to solve this last problem but the fact remained that I was alone and unformed. I must have looked a soggy, frightened wreck when I got off that plane, but Anthony received me like I was the very answer to his unasked question.

'Here I am,' I said.

'Here you are,' he beamed.

I went home with him that night, partly because I didn't have anywhere else to go, partly because we were pawns in a crime that drew us together, and partly because he was so eager for me to read his latest screenplay, 'The Devil's Razor Strap.' It turned out this was only one out of fifty or sixty unproduced screenplays Anthony had written. He'd neatly stacked his work in various draft form around the basement. The only other thing down there aside from those towers of paper was a twin mattress on the floor. This bed was very neatly made. His room reminded me of a monk's cell, a picture of devotion.

Gently, gently, he helped me cut away the packs of coke duct taped around my midsection, thighs and calves. He pointed his scissors at my wrist and asked about the ratty red ribbon. I explained that a beggar woman had tied it there on the steps of Igreja do Bomfim, knotting it three times with a warning that if I ever removed it my wishes would not come true, whereas if I let it unravel on its own, they might. Years had passed and the ribbon was still intact. I was so sick of wearing it, I told Anthony, but I believed in magic just enough not to cut it off.

'What did you wish for?' Anthony asked.

'I can't tell you specifically,' I said. 'But I can tell you generally. The first wish was for success. The second was for family. And the third was for love.'

Anthony surprised me then by taking a great risk. In every way, it was greater than the risk I'd just taken as a courier of narcotics. He grabbed my hand and snipped off the ribbon.

'That was a bold move,' I huffed, unsure if I wanted to stab him or hug him.

Later on he built me a giant aquarium, bought a star in my name, and hired a mariachi band to serenade me. But really, he won me with this initial gesture.

'I promise you,' he bluffed, still holding my hand, 'that all your wishes will come true.'

Anthony held my hand on the day before the baby was due while the midwife swept my membranes. May 20, a Friday. The anticipation was killing us. Neither one of us could quite believe our good fortune. We'd made a little money by this point, enough to buy a small apartment at the top of Manhattan in the shadow of the George Washington Bridge. The windows looked out on an alleyway rather than the Hudson River, but still. It was ours. We didn't buy it with dirty money, either. We bought it with the money Anthony made for *Amsterdamned!*, the screenplay he wrote in a fit of inspiration on our honeymoon in the Netherlands. Its plotline savaging Zwarte Piete didn't translate across cultures. The movie went straight to video but that was okay. We were too excited about what was going down in my uterus to be disappointed by anything else.

So the midwife had two fingers deep in my vagina. I looked up at the mobile strung from the curtain rod in the bay window behind the couch. It was my favourite gift from the baby shower because it was homemade – a pinecone, a spool, a prism, a shell. The other gifts and baby things were carefully arranged and folded on a tall shelf in the hallway. The ruffled bassinet waited next to our bed. The pack of maxi pads doused in witch hazel to soothe my battered postpartum crotch were cooling in the freezer next to the Tupperware containers full of frozen soups and stews to sustain us through the first exhausting weeks. The cabbage whose leaves would relieve my engorged breasts waited in the fridge. The pink plastic sitz bath sat next to the toilet. The inflatable birthing pool was boxed with its electric pump in Anthony's office. The basket of clean rags and towels was tucked beneath his writing desk. And on top of his desk lay several envelopes stuffed with letters to slip under our neighbours' doors. He didn't want anyone thinking he was beating on his wife if I screamed, or worry that I was in danger.

*Greetings! I am writing to share the good news that Emma is in labor with our first child. We are doing a home birth. If you hear strange noises coming from our apartment, please don't be alarmed.*

Most people *were* alarmed we'd opted to give birth at home. Namely, our mothers, which was why they weren't invited. We didn't need their nervous energy upsetting the scene. My mom delivered my brother and me in the hospital and believed, unsurprisingly, that I should do the same with my child. 'Dad was born at home,' I reminded her, to get her off my back. He was caught by a woman called Nan Ophelia, the midwife who delivered all the black babies in that part of the Mississippi Delta. 'Not by choice,' my mother reminded me. 'It was Jim Crow. The white hospitals refused them. That was then. This is now. What are you thinking, honey? Your pain threshold is so low. You used to cry over paper cuts and when you bit your tongue. This will be ten million times worse. God forbid, what if something goes wrong?'

'Why should anything go wrong?' I countered.

Anthony's mother was even more mystified. She came from Uganda, had run from the backward hospital in

146

the capital with its crowds of women writhing on the floor, its placenta pit, its bribes and its flies, among other wretched things, and never looked back. She couldn't comprehend why we refused this one comfort of the first world. 'The Dutch do it this way,' I reasoned. 'And the other mammals. The whales and the lions. Why not me?' But my mother-in-law only shook her head. 'You know that it's going to hurt, don't you? My dear, it's going to pain you like nothing you could imagine. My grandchild's sweet head will tear you from your hoo-hoo to your bumhole.'

The old Dominican women around the way were no better. 'Sin drogas, mi hija, por qué?' they grilled me on the street or in line at the Quisqueyana Deli. Was it that my husband couldn't afford the doctor? Labour was a curse best slept through and forgotten. The drugs were a triumph over suffering, they said. Why be a martyr?

To prove to myself I am brave, I told them. That was the main thing. To feel the most ordinary of miracles. To have an accomplishment to boast about that wasn't bullshit. To be able to carry the knowledge of my own strength with me for the rest of my life.

But those women took a perverse pleasure in telling me my life, as I knew it, was about to be over. That after the baby came I would never be free from worry again. They told me to get to the hospital right then, that very second, I looked ready to go, I looked like I was carrying twins, I was big as the earth itself, I was carrying low, I was carrying a boy. I would recognise his face and never remember not knowing it. They offered me blessings. They offered me unsolicited advice. They lay their hands on my belly and told me I could kiss my sex life goodbye.

Inside my vagina I felt a vague tugging. 'I am circling the crown of baby's head,' smiled the midwife, who was well-regarded, fifty, Chinese and no-nonsense. 'Your cervix is softer than butter. I can feel the tops of your baby's ears.'

'What does that mean?' Anthony asked. 'Is that normal?' He squeezed my hand in his. One of our hands was sweaty, I couldn't tell whose.

'Emma is fully effaced,' the midwife explained.

'A face?' asked Anthony.

I hoped the baby would have his hair, my eyesight, his cheekbones, my ears.

'It's fine,' I said, interlacing my fingers with his like the teeth of a zipper. We'd learned in class that birth was ninety per cent mind. After so much waiting, we were finally going to see our baby's face and that was nothing but wonderful. It was time for 'positive affirmation', for 'refusing fear', for 'mind over matter', for the powerful sincerity of clichés. I said, 'The baby will come when it's ready to come.'

I knew the baby was riding low, had been feeling the pressure of his head behind my pubic bone for days. I felt he was moulding himself, preparing to make his grand entrance. But I also knew that most mothers delivered their first babies sometime beyond their due dates. And maybe, in spite of all our preparation, a part of me was counting on that extra time to ponder the alien thing that possessed me. I was incubating a real live person. I couldn't really comprehend this truth.

'Everything's progressing normally,' the midwife confirmed. She had a midwifery conference to attend in Texas on the twenty-fourth. She'd promised that if I gestated long, she would cancel the trip, but here she was with her agenda, intervening to make the baby come as scheduled. When she pulled out her fingers there was blood on her rubber glove. That too was normal, she said, before deciding to send me to Kang to help move things along.

Suddenly I was nervous. She was rushing me. I realised I was going to have a baby imminently. And, if we were blessed, the baby would always be there, would never not be. Sweet Jesus, we would no longer be without a baby. 'Who's Kang?' I asked. 'And why do we need to move things along if everything's normal?'

'My acupuncturist,' the midwife answered. She pressed my knee, firmly. 'It's time. He'll see you tonight at 5.00.' She scribbled his address in Chinatown on her pad, tore off the page, checked my blood pressure, told me to call her if I felt anything, and was gone.

Anthony held my hand on the A train down to Chinatown. He held my hand at 42nd Street where the conductor barked we had to switch trains due to track work. He held my hand in Times Square where we moved through the rush hour crush of tourists, taxicabs, pickpockets, panhandlers, buskers, hustlers, street preachers, theatregoers, pigeons, drunks and crazies holding homemade signs: THE END IS NIGH. I enjoyed my volume, the real estate I took up on the ridiculously crowded sidewalk, the way my husband protected me with his arm, the way New York City parted for us like the Red Sea.

'This is the last walk I will take as a childless woman,' I thought. 'Every walk I will take from now on, I will be somebody's mother.' I was so much more overwhelmed by this thought than the out-of-towners were by the spectacle of Times Square. But something in the posture of their upturned heads as they craned their necks for the blaring, blinking billboard lights was in sync with my feeling of awe, my awful feeling. My senses were overloaded, scrambled. I could taste the tourists' perfume. I could hear the shutters clacking on their Japanese cameras. I could feel my baby revolving his head. I could see my husband's jumpy nerves and the bright explosions of the honking car horns. A cartoonist beckoned us to sit and have our caricatures drawn. A comedian pleaded with us to take an electric blue flier advertising his stand-up show. A hot dog vendor barked at a man with a tambourine standing in his customers' way. A footless diabetic banged out his story with drumsticks on an upside-down bucket.

'Heaven will be better than this world!' cried a woman under the giant pointing hand outside the wax museum. She held a white bullhorn to her mouth and appeared in her floral smock, for lack of a better term, Midwestern. 'Repent! The flames of the apocalypse are licking at your ankles and you do not know it.'

'Shut up, lady,' a businessman yelled.

'Repent, sinner!' she screamed. 'The world ends tomorrow. The earth will crack and storms will sweep the seas. Only those born again in His name will be redeemed. So it is written and so it shall pass. I am trying to save you from the fire and the flood! Repent and be saved! You!' she spotted me. 'Yes, you with the unborn child. Do you hear me? Your world is about to be over and done.'

Anthony looked ready to pop her in the mouth. Instead he tugged at my hand and led me back underground to catch another train. It was sweltering down there. It was the first circle of hell. There were too many people yapping, shoving, piping loud music into their ears to block each other out. 'You okay?' Anthony asked, his eyebrows knitted in concern. I nodded, but it was getting even harder, if that was possible, to walk. I had a bowling ball in my pelvic girdle; I could barely lift my legs. I was dense enough to sink into the subway platform, then the seat somebody relinquished on the Q train, then the massage table at the acupuncturist's.

Anthony kept hold of my hand while Kang, in a tight room in a tenement next to a seafood store on Mott Street, officiously read my tongue, pressed his thumbs against the dark circles under my eyes, stretched me out on a table, pummelled my back, stuck needles in my head, hands, legs and feet to direct the energy of my blood, and covered me like a marathon runner with a silver foil blanket. I fell into a deep aquatic sleep and dreamed about fish. When I woke up at seven Anthony was still holding my hand. I could feel the overhead light buzzing in my teeth. 'Let's get you home, darling,' he said.

Again, the train. What per cent of our lives in this city do we spend underground in its bowels? The longest uninterrupted stretch of subway track in New York runs on the A line between 59th Street, Columbus Circle and 125th Street in Harlem. Since the A train makes no stops between those two points, it attains its full speed on that ride. Twenty-five miles an hour may not be very fast but the A, compared with all the other trains, flies like a rocket. The wheels shriek on the tracks as the cars plunge forward. Children like to plant themselves in the grimy front window of the first car to watch the dark tunnel unfurling beneath the train's headlights. They press their foreheads against the glass and pretend they're conducting the voyage. I've done it myself. It's exhilarating. But on that night, the train's wild swaying made me feel the opposite. The faster it barrelled, the more drained I became.

I was moving, I was being moved, and within me was motion. The train was a drunken cradle. I felt every bump, every shudder, and every blasted curve. My back was so sore. My sacrum, in particular, felt manhandled by the seat of hard grey plastic. The commotion of my bones and blood had me stunned. I felt a throbbing in my core. The clatter of the train rearranged my atoms until I was no longer myself. Dizzy, I was the train. I lay my head on my husband's shoulder and silently began to cry.

After a small eternity we arrived at our stop and somehow ascended to the level of the street. The sun slid down gorgeously, like a postcard of a sunset. I have to remember this, I thought, but I was already forgetting. Behind the bridge, the sky streaked pinkward to the Jersey horizon. Around us the apartment buildings glowed in the saturated golden light. Their bricks looked softer than usual. My edges also were blurring. I had to stop moving or I would seep into my elongated shadow on the gum-freckled sidewalk. I had to pin my shadow's feet with my shoes and close my eyes to keep myself together.

'Are you having a contraction?' Anthony asked. His hand was an anchor. If it wasn't for my husband's hand I might have turned into a puddle.

'I don't know,' I groaned. I thought the contractions would feel menstrual, a vice-like clamping isolated to my uterus, but what I felt, I felt with my entire body. Everybody told me labour would hurt, but what I felt was unlike any pain I'd experienced before. It was ignited from within rather than inflicted from without. Not like heat but what makes heat hot. That burning entropy belonged to me. I knew how to run away from pain by clenching my teeth, tightening my abdomen, shrugging my shoulders, fisting my fingers, or holding my breath. But this, I had to step toward. It was happening. I couldn't protect myself from it and I didn't want to. Rather than curling inward like a snail into its shell, I would have to unfurl myself like a wave spreading onto the shore. I steadied myself to turn inside out by loosening my limbs.

'I can't wait to meet you,' I exhaled. I opened my eyes and looked at my husband, the constellation of freckles across the bridge of his nose.

'You beautiful superhero,' he smiled.

And then I was ready to walk again.

Once inside the apartment I slipped out of my shapeless maternity dress, turned off the bathroom light, drew myself a bath and stretched into the warm water. The island of my belly contorted, convulsed. I watched my linea negra bend like a bow. Time passed. This was the first stage, Anthony reminded me. It would probably last a while – hours, maybe even days. He hovered big and helpless above me. 'What should I do?' he asked. 'Should I time it?'

I nodded and began to moan. It was eight thirty. Then it was nine and dark outside. The contractions seemed to be five minutes apart. Then three minutes. I could talk. And then I couldn't.

'I don't know if I'm doing it right,' Anthony said, fumbling with his watch. 'It's happening too fast.'

'Call the midwife,' I told him.

What happened next is a blur. I can only remember it in uncontained bursts, out of sequence and, except for a jumble of inadequate metaphors, beyond description. But I will try.

I remember Anthony holding his cell phone to my head so that the midwife could hear the sounds I made. She'd been watching a movie in a theatre downtown when he called. She doubted I was as far along as he suggested, even when she heard my voice. I think I lowed like a cow. I believe I tried every vowel and settled on O. She told him to call her again in an hour. By that point I was on my hands and knees in the water, tilting my pelvis forward and back. I remember Anthony disappearing in the back room to blow up the birthing pool, coming back to announce there was a part missing, disappearing again to put on the mix of songs he'd compiled for the occasion. The majority of the songs were by Metallica. I think I asked him to turn the music down before yelling at him to turn it off. I remember him reporting, with great relief, that the midwife was now in a taxi heading home to fetch her supplies and that she expected to arrive in Washington Heights, if traffic allowed, sometime after 11.00.

I remember radiating heat. I remember how good it felt when Anthony placed a cold washcloth on my forehead and another around the back of my neck. I remember how bad it felt when he coaxed me out of the tub to the toilet to empty my bladder, and that I wanted only to get right back into the water for the weightlessness it offered me. Fuck, I said. I kept saying it, *fuck, fuck*, like a thumb flicking a lighter. It was the best word because it was hard, it was what I had done and what I had gotten into by doing it, and because what I was doing now was so very hard. I remember my belly pointing like a football. I remember sipping coconut water through a straw in a blue cup.

Around midnight Anthony called the midwife again. She didn't pick up. I could hear his fear when he left her a message. Then I vomited over the side of the tub and the room tilted like a ship. The nausea came at me in waves that surged with greater and greater strength until the moments of relief between surges thinned to nothing and I could no longer hear the current of traffic on the bridge or the corner boys playing reggaeton outside and I could no longer speak. I knew this was the transition stage, the shortest and hardest part, the point of no return, the void. It was May 21. The skin of my belly was tight as a drum. Soon I would have to push, whether the midwife came or not.

'Breathe,' Anthony reminded me, 'breathe.'

We breathed.

Then again, the nausea. The nausea was the worst part. It carried me toward a black hole wherein my mind revolved and collapsed without room for thought. But to be unthinking was strangely freeing. I became sloppy, leather-lunged, loud. My throat was so hoarse from groaning. I used the ragged sound to bring my baby down. I visualised the vibration of my voice pulling him like a string as I steadied myself to push. I tucked my chin to my chest, planted my feet, held on to my knees, lifted my hips and opened my thighs like a book. I was Pangæa, coming undone. I felt the intense pressure of my baby's head nearly rending me apart, the tectonic plates of my pelvis shifting to allow for his passage. I pictured him moving like a train, rounding the curve of Carus, sliding through the ring of fire.

'I have to push,' I told Anthony.

'Are you sure?' he asked, but I was already doing it. With each surge, I pushed again.

'Do you see the head yet?' I asked between surges.

'Not yet,' my husband said. He stood on his knees next to the bathtub in a half inch of water that sloshed over onto the tiles, his pants sopping, his glasses fogged, his face a picture of concentration.

'Is he coming?' I panted.

'I think so,' Anthony said.

'You think so?'

'He's coming,' he said more decisively. 'You're doing great.'

I pushed again. I felt I was taking the biggest shit of all time.

'Don't you see the head now?' I begged.

'Not yet,' Anthony apologised.

'You've got to be kidding me,' I shouted.

I pushed again, but really the baby was pushing himself. I hollered to bring him down. I remember the water bag finally bursting right before he crowned, a satisfyingly warm volcanic gush. Later Anthony told me the baby's head behind the bag of waters looked like a dark ostrich egg, the tiny hairs waving like cilia on clay. Clay's head was out, underwater. We didn't yet know he was a he. He turned his head to make way for his shoulders. Then with a roaring terrible cleavage that was the multiplication of my self, I pushed out the rest of him.

Anthony lifted our son out of the bathwater like a trophy. He laughed, a little maniacally, placed him on my chest and kissed me. The baby bleated like a lamb and opened his dark eyes. I marvelled at that head, the way the hair whorled like Van Gogh's starry night. I checked between the legs. Here was our son. I gave a great sigh of relief and gratitude. He rooted into me, grabbing at my breast as if to make sure I was real. Amazed, Anthony said 'You did it.'

In the days that followed we lost all track of time. What with the sleep deprivation, the isolation, the mess of diapers, piles of dirty laundry and dishes, the bloody nipples, the lapses into panic, the stab of love, the incontinence, the incoherence, the endless nursing and the baby's reversal of night and day, it was hard to say exactly how many days had passed. I couldn't say whether, when we finally ventured out of the apartment with Anthony holding Clay in his arms like a fragile lamp, and me taking tiny mincing geisha steps along 181st Street toward the river for our first walk as a family, only to discover at the graffitied lookout point over the West Side Highway that the bridge had collapsed into the water, I was dreaming or not. All I know is that those women were right.

Everything had changed.

But they were also wrong. I didn't recognise my son's face at all when my husband first handed him to me. He looked like a turtle, purplish and gray and totally alien. And I wasn't gobsmacked by love when I first met him. Not instantly. In that moment, still steeping in the water, I was just relieved to be done birthing him. I remember thinking his feet looked like cashews. I remember the surprisingly rubbery texture of the umbilical cord and that when the placenta bloomed out of me chased by a red parachute of blood it was time to separate him. Anthony clamped the cord close to the baby's belly with one of my barrettes and prepared to cut it. His hand shook with the scissors as if with delirium tremens. Adrenaline and terror, mixed. Clay's colour changed like a mood ring from gray to pink. Me, I rode that good raft of oxytocin, feeling the child squirm against me. Pain was the wrong word. I was just so motherfucking proud.

'Maybe we should wait for the midwife,' Anthony paused.

I knew by then she wasn't coming. The world as we knew it had come to an end. 'I promise you,' I bluffed, 'everything's gonna be alright.'

And then my husband cut the cord.

# Capturing Rapture

I wrote this story shortly after giving birth to my first child on 21 May 2011, predicted as the end of days by Christian radio broadcaster Harold Camping. He maintained that after the righteous flew up to heaven there would follow five months of plagues, fire and brimstone on Earth, with millions dying each day, culminating with the end of the world. I spent the end of my pregnancy spotting signs around New York City pronouncing my son's due date as the apocalypse. While these signs didn't cause me alarm, they did remind me of the momentous change I was about to undergo. At the same time, I encountered some pretty fierce judgements from women close to me about my decision to birth at home (fewer than one per cent of women do so in the US). I kept insisting that I was looking forward to the event and they kept telling me I was insane.

My husband and I took a Bradley Method birthing class like the one described in the story to prepare us for a natural birth. The instructor invited two women from a previous class to share their birth stories with us one night. I was moved to tears by what they shared but my husband was bored by their unprofessional storytelling. While I felt he missed the point entirely, I had to agree that making a narrative out of childbirth is a difficult challenge. Really, the experience is beyond language and structure. But I wanted to craft a story with the tools of fiction that would honour the enormously empowering adventure of giving birth. I also wanted to convey the seismic sensations of a body in labour in Biblical, apocalyptic and rapturous proportion. Finally, I wanted to be the hero.

Emma is a character whose perspective I've written from before. In fact, she's the protagonist of my first novel, which closes with her leaving America for Brazil. I don't think of Emma as me but as my fictional double, a vessel through which I can make narrative sense out of the profound or confusing elements of my life, often so that I can lay them to rest. I expect I'll return to her again and again for this purpose, as Hemingway did with Nick Adams, Philip Roth with Nathan Zuckerman, and John Updike with his Rabbit.

To varying degrees, all fiction writers draw from their autobiographies to authenticate their work. When I was a graduate student in Creative Writing, I was taught by a novelist named Chuck Wachtel. He impressed this idea upon our writing workshop by assigning a haunting short, short story called 'Crossing the River Zbrucz' by Isaac Babel, along with one of the entries collected in Babel's *1920 Diary*. Read together, it's clear that Babel drew details directly from his diary to vivify the story. The difference between the journal entry and the short story is structure. Real life is chaotic and, if not meaningless, plotless. Plot is the thing we impose upon real life to create story. In an effort to help other writers and students of Creative Writing think about how to plot stories drawn from real life, I'll describe the steps I took to write 'Rapture'.

## Choosing a subject

First, I chose a dramatic subject I knew would recede from my memory if I didn't write it down quickly. The instructor from our birthing class, who we later hired to be our doula, encouraged everyone in the class to write our birth stories. We would suffer afterward from amnesia, she warned, a

160

biological forgetfulness designed to enable us to bear more children in the future. She also assigned *Ina May's Guide to Childbirth* as a textbook. It was full of such stories, told from the mother's perspective. In the final stages of my pregnancy I read this book each night before going to bed. It gave me a picture of what to expect. As a whole, the stories it contained were a testament to the resilient power of women's bodies. I realised while reading these stories that I hadn't encountered such graphic descriptions of birth in literature before, if I had encountered them at all. They helped prepare me to tell my own birth story by making it seem a worthwhile subject. But really, as my husband pointed out, these weren't actually stories. They were descriptions of the situation of labour. The women who wrote them were describing a great change, but not showing the ways in which they were changed themselves. I decided I would use fiction to write my birth story instead.

*Finding source material*

Second, I turned to my journal for details. The journal I kept when I was pregnant was a gift from my husband. He bought it for me in Amsterdam, where we lived during my first and second trimester. It is a thin soft-covered journal with black binding, lined pages and a picture of a steer on the cover. Under the steer, my husband wrote 'The Noodle'. (This is what we called the baby until he was born because he was the size of a macaroni noodle when we first found out about him.) The Noodle was to be the subject of the journal. I used it to record information during prenatal visits with our Dutch midwife, and then later, after we returned to New York, I continued using it for note-taking during the birthing class and the home visits from the midwife who eventually delivered our son. It's full of medical and biological information, phone numbers and addresses to use in the event of an emergency, lists of food rich in iron and protein as well as food and drugs that risked the foetus's well-being, notes on the stages of labour, techniques for managing pain, recommended titles on parenting and other details related to birth in general.

But the journal also contains more personal entries unique to my individual experience, not all of which have to do with birth. These include observations about racism in the Netherlands, directions for bicycling along the city's canals, lists of boy and girl names we were considering, a grievance against my husband for not being more forgiving of my hormone-induced bad moods, and mantras I invented to stay focused during labour. Very few of these details were relevant for my story, but I hope the ones I selected made it more particular. Going through the journal was an exercise in remembering physical and emotional details about being pregnant, details I wouldn't have retained if I hadn't written them down.

### Interviewing others

Third, I asked my husband and the women who assisted my son's birth what surprised them most about the event. (In the story Emma and Anthony deliver the child on their own. In reality, four amazing women helped me and my husband.) Here is what they shared: The doula was surprised by my sense of calm. The midwife was surprised when I said, 'That wasn't so bad,' immediately afterward. The midwife's assistant was surprised when I politely asked her not to use our nice towels to mop up the goop coming out of me. My sister-in-law was surprised by how far along

I was when she arrived at our apartment. And my husband was surprised by what our son's head looked like right before the bag of waters burst. Some of these details also made their way into my story. Asking for other perspectives gave me a more objective picture of what happened and helped me think of myself as a character.

*Drawing an outline*
Fourth, I mapped out the story's beginning, middle and end. I thought of it initially in three acts. Act one, the birthing class, would introduce the concept of the Rapture. Act two, the labour and delivery, would suggest that something unexpected took place outside to prevent the midwife from showing up to do her job. Act three, the family's first walk outdoors, would reveal that the Rapture did in fact occur. I knew that the second act would be the longest, and that I wanted the George Washington Bridge to have fallen down in the third. I also knew that at its heart this story was about the cataclysmic transformation of becoming a parent. During the plotting stage I allowed my imagination to begin playing and to untether the story from reality.

*Writing a draft*
Fifth, I sat down to write in a café around the corner so as not to be interrupted by my baby's needs. My husband watched him for two hours every morning for the two weeks it took me to complete the piece. Some things I hadn't anticipated came up during the process of writing. The setting of New York City became an important element. The couple's back-story (almost completely invented) seemed vital to include. And I realised after

dramatising the birth that the ending should be more subtle than what I originally envisioned – more suggestive than explicit. I wanted to leave it up to the reader's interpretation whether or not the Rapture took place. The story's real Rapture is what happens to the woman's body, so rather than linger on the collapsed bridge, I cycled back to her body at the end. The story-within-the-story about the red string her husband cut off her wrist provided me with a new structure. I chose to echo that crucial moment of risk and promise by finishing with the husband cutting the cord.

### Revising and editing

Finally, I edited what I had written. I shared the story with a trusted writer-friend for feedback and implemented some of her suggestions. I read it over and over and over again, tweaking the language, re-ordering information and cutting extraneous sentences. During the time I spent editing, two natural disasters visited New York City, each of them highly unusual in these parts. The first was an earthquake. The second was a hurricane.

# 8 Amal Chatterjee

## *A simple recipe*

### IN WHICH WE MEET, ARE MARRIED AND BEGIN OUR LIFE TOGETHER

Sachin. Husband, breadwinner. Suited and booted like his grandmother wouldn't have believed. How times change. Two generations and paddy fields are as alien – and as familiar – as wine groves. Vineyards, isn't that what they're called properly? Who cares. Sachin, Calcutta born and bred, cultivated a taste for wine. I went along like I did with everything else.

We were perfectly matched. Brown eye for brown eye, wheatish complexion for clear skin, you could say limb for limb, brain cell for brain cell, MA for MBA, but no-one said that, they checked on star for star instead. Not star sign for star sign, as we in college did, instructed by Linda Whatshername, American guru we greedily devoured, no, this was the real thing, astrologers let loose on our birth details while parents did the other homework, checking us out in person. His family inscrutable and cautious, mine nervous, hiding their enthusiasm badly. Making me think then and later, ungratefully amused, maybe they should have married each other instead, my mum his pop, my dad his mom? He and I called them that in private to distinguish between the pairs. A private joke, of course, they were Ma and Baba to their faces, Our Parents, His Parents, Her Parents, My Parents otherwise, but when we were alone, educated people lapsing into English ever more often as we only ever read in our acquired tongue, he thrillers, I clever novels, glossy magazines, mom and pop, mum and dad.

Perfect matchingness. Compatibility in aspirations. Complementarity. He was minting an MBA, in its final throes when first contact was made. I didn't have to stand by being supportive, I was after BA, in MA, BM, Before Marriage. When I and my girlfriends were biding time, padding out our bridal biodata. No thought of career, not me at least, I was content to anticipate, comfortably, traditionally, the prospect of my own household.

A flat to keep, servants to organise, soon children to wash, brush, scold, feed, put to bed.

Warm milk with sugar in it, Didima's remedies relayed by phone.

While He went out to work. Dinner together unless he was late or away, the children tucked in, we'd turn on the TV. News, Hollywood, Hindi films, the occasional worthy other. Probably nothing French or too artsy, leave alone khadi-wearer passion-inducing. He'd wear suits and ties, spend his days in air-conditioned offices and cars and my mother or his would take the children when we went out for an evening. Or we'd leave them with ayah – though where would we find a good one these days, one that one could really trust?

While he steadily mounted the corporate ladder, definitely the corporate, not the dull certainty of Government service for us. The future was the private sector, the economy was turning around, a behemoth groaning to life.

And so we were matched, Man and Wife. Husband and Wife. Never Woman alone was I, stepping straight from Girl to Wife, passing only Betrothal in between. Even as a twenty-something pre-marriage, I stayed Girl. While He proceeded from Boy to Man, to Man and Engaged, to Groom and Man, finally Man and Husband. At the same time as I did nothing. That's the way it is for men.

Not Karma, I chose my path, my fate. Why not? No career for me, but being a wife isn't idleness. I saw the house to keep, the family to look after. On the side, house and family permitting, perhaps some social responsibility. Charity work. Teaching, fund-raising, something like that. Nothing that interfered with His smooth rise to fortune.

Our families found us agreeable.

Nobody, however, thought about the kitchen, least of all me. Leaving me to ask, beg, wheedle, practise. Practise most of all.

*Luchi*
the way they made it at home
Not by my mother, she didn't actually cook herself, she presided over her kitchen, but this is what she presided over. Warm water, I learned. Room-temperature warm, not hot warm. The colder the climate, the warmer the water needed, the opposite of pastry dough which needs ice-cold.

*Sift the flour.* I dispense with that often enough. On one's own, why bother? So it'll be a little heavier, who cares? If there are any creepy-crawlies in it, I throw the whole lot out, don't waste my time. It's only flour, after all. *Add the water and the salt, knead into a dough* that is neither sticky nor breaks, the consistency of Plasticine only softer. *Rest*

167

*under a damp cloth for fifteen–twenty minutes. Divide into balls* you can almost cup your fingers round when they are held in the palm. *Roll out into circles about 3mm thick.* Travelled so far and wide, I can now measure in metric. *Heat oil in a karahi or deep pan.* We used Dalda at home but I've learned any good, clean oil will do. Almost any. *Drop luchis in one at a time*, ducking them with a slotted spoon. *Remove with slotted spoon, drain in a colander or on a rack. Serve immediately.* With dal or ghugni or spicy potatoes. Vegetables.

Easy, isn't it? Growing up I didn't learn that though, didn't have any interest. India wasn't Shining yet, it wasn't even glowing dimly. There were, there'd always be, servants.

Things didn't quite turn out that way.

But first, Him, my Significant Other. More accurately, The Significant, I was Other. Sachinananda Bhattacharya. Sachin to some, Bhatta to his buddies, Bubun to his family. When I married, I did as all good girls, I moved into his house. Which, in those days, was my in-laws'. All of a room assigned to us. Precisely as I expected. In time, so the plan went, another floor would be added, to provide accommodation for the families of the sons. Elder Brother Rabindranath (my in-laws were nothing if not ambitious) didn't do as expected though. Contrary to his name, he joined the Army, providing him reason to be away from home often, almost always. Captain Rising (my private in-head name for him), dashing (the mothers' description, not mine) in his uniform, he displayed no inclination to marry. The Army, he said, was all the family he needed. There was little anyone could say; each generation of Bhattacharyas had a confirmed bachelor, his father's younger brother before him, his second eldest great-uncle before that, goodness knows who before.

Only, times had changed. One bachelor in a litter of at least three or four sons was one thing, the elder of just two was cause for concern. Fortunately for all, Sachinananda, assigned to me and me to him, wasn't averse to the idea of carrying on the family name.

So we were carried round the sacred flame seven times, I placed the sweetmeat in his mouth, women ululated around me and men got on with talking business and comparing offspring's achievements. And, after a wakeful night, we caught the train to Darjeeling for our honeymoon. Where, Darjeeling-like, it rained for days, broad sheets of water driving across the Mall. We took refuge in – or rather, rarely ventured forth from – our hotel.

We made it back still married and ready to begin.

Our room was on the first floor. A single room. En-suite, it had been intended for Rabindranath's family but, since he had none, it was ours. Most of it a vast bed. Four-poster, dark brown, carved headboard. An heirloom. Dunlopillo mattress, crisp white sheets. Starched. Foam pillows, Bihar Emporium bedcover. I would change that. Shuttered windows, cream on the inside, dusty green out. Ornamental flat metal grill with flower motif. Ancient dark teak dresser with ornamented mirror frame, the mirror itself, another heirloom, flecked over the years. Metal trunks under a quilt I always intended to replace. Godrej lockable steel almirah. European-style commode and calcium-caked steel shower in the white-tiled bathroom. White Sanitaryware sink. Nothing, in other words, out of the ordinary. No more, no less than one might expect. His parents had the best room, of course, view over the wall of the park beyond.

Only – what was I to do? My MA was concluded, an MPhil not on the cards. His mother, Ma I called her as I ought, ruled the household, had no use for me. She had wanted an educated daughter-in-law, not a home-trained one and she had what she had asked for. So to my own devices I was left.

Books. Books. More books. I began where I'd left off as a teenager. Agatha Christie. P. G. Wodehouse. Mills and Boon. Yes, I'll admit to the last, even if I didn't last with them. It wasn't the formula, it just wasn't me. Paul Theroux crept up on me, enthralled me as he travelled misanthropically. Isabel Allende and Amy Tan. I was discovering worlds.

'... Delhi office...' he was saying.

That got my attention. I put my book down and sat up. 'Delhi?'

'I'll go ahead,' he said, 'Get acclimatised...'

I didn't hear the rest. My mind was awhirl. Transfer? A place of our own! No more grandmother's bed and dresser, steel almirah?

'... Naturally, I said I'd talk it over with you. It'd take us away from the family ...'

Who gave a damn about the family?! I didn't say that, instead I asked, 'When?'

'Next month, if I can.'

'Of course we can.'

He was proud of me. I was the Wife he'd wanted, unafraid of the Corporate World. I'd held my own at the first reception, politely but correctly drunk Thums Up while he drank whisky. Modern, but not too. Not yet, not until we were on our own, had our own space. Which was now on the cards.

Gurgaon. The car sent for us sped along brightly-lit highways, weaving through the traffic with the confidence of a regular. Darkness was falling rapidly and the giant steel and glass buildings on either side came alive with light, thousands of windows glowing self-confidence. Sachin revelled in it.

'This is the future! Calcutta has no idea, this is where it is...'

The company had assigned us a flat. The car pulled off the highway, past high walls and multiplicationally higher towers topped with cupolas and temples, drew up at wrought-iron the height of embassy gates.

A uniformed man tapped the window.

'Block D, E11.' The man returned to his cabin, consulted a ledger. Then, nodding, he reached out, pressed a button. The giant gates swung open slowly and he saluted as we drove past.

Ground floor car parks punctuated by smart entrance lobbies, each with a bank of bells and a uniformed guard, the logo of the estate emblazoned on their peaked caps.

Block D. Another guard stepped up to the car, held it open for Sachin first, then came round to me.

'Salaam Memsaab.'

Sachin pressed a note into the driver's hand.

'Luggage lejaao.'

The guard and the driver hefted the suitcases out of the boot. 'Ha ji.'

Of course. We couldn't be expected to carry them ourselves. Sachin, who'd been on recon, led the way through the open (reinforced glass, sliding, totally secure, bulletproof even, left open for convenience) doors. A

171

modern lift, red electronic numerals. E11 was on the second floor. Ten floors below the penthouse. Some day.

'What do you think?' he asked, swinging the front door open and turning on the light.

In spite of myself, I gasped. The space! A living room half the size of the entire floor at my in-laws yawned ahead. To the left, two doors, one ajar, a bed visible within. Ahead, sofas – two! – and a coffee table. To the right, a brief corridor with two doors on the left, one on the right and one at the end. I did a quick calculation in my head. Even if one door led to a kitchen, another to one of the bathrooms and one (a guess) to storage, that left three more rooms...

'I thought you said two bedrooms?'

'I did. There's a pantry and a study too.'

I'd left it all up to him. This was to be temporary, if things worked out (and why wouldn't they?), we'd begin looking for something of our own in a couple of months. Meanwhile...

'Wow!'

'I'll take that to mean you approve,' he grinned, 'I told you I could manage.'

A voice behind us. 'Sahib?' The guard with the bags. Sachin beckoned him in, pressed bakshish into his hand. The man slipped it with practised ease into his pocket, salaamed. 'Welcome, Memsaab.' I nodded and he sidled out, shutting the door softly behind. Well-trained!

'Wait till you see the view.'

Between the tower blocks, a lawn stretched, manicured, a play area for children at one end, neat street-like lights lighting up the asphalt paths around. A woman in a white sari walked a white Pekinese, two old men sat silently side by side on a bench. A car drove slowly past, ducked into the parking, turned its lights off. A man in a suit stepped out, locked the doors and made for the entrance of Block G.

Not the sound of dogs barking, not nearby at least. Yes, the sounds of traffic, heavy but distant, like low thunder punctuated by weary horns. Far away, almost drowned by the sound of a cricket nearby.

'Wow!' I said again.

'My secretary has arranged a maid for now,' he said.

His secretary arranged the maid!

'We don't have to keep her, of course,' he went on, 'It's just to get us started. Better value than a cleaning company.'

A cleaning company?! 'Of course.' I left him behind, went into the bedroom. Double bed, neat, unassuming. No family heirloom teak here, thank goodness. Instead, cane chairs by the bed, His and Hers reading lamps and side-tables. No dresser though, but I could live without. For now, not for long. We could afford it all.

I went into the bathroom. Not quite right, this. Plain and functional, grimy high window opening into a shaft. A surprised (indignant?) cockroach fled down the drain.

'We need Phenyl,' I said stoutly.

'Send the maid out tomorrow,' he said, coming up behind me. 'She speaks Bengali, by the way.' He knew my comfort zone. Hindi isn't my thing, Punjabi's beyond me.

She was shy, a slip of a girl, thousands of miles further from home than I. Bangladesh is another country even if we speak the language. But she knew the way around, I didn't.

'Where's the bazar?' I asked her next morning, after he'd gone.

She smiled, almost. 'Bazar? No bazar, Didi, shops outside the compound.' She called it 'compound', we residents called it 'estate'. Estate doesn't sound so good in many languages.

So to the shops I went. The cycle rickshaw offered to wait, pressed me to allow him, but fool once, I wasn't going to be fool twice. It'd have taken me all of five minutes to walk there once out of the gates. Longer from Block D but cycle rickshaws weren't allowed in unless they already had passengers.

A vegetable *shop*. Not a stall, not a string of stalls, just the one shop with produce on shelves, prices on neat labels.

'That much for potatoes?'

The shop owner shook his head sadly. 'Prices, madame, they are upward going.' My Hindi had failed so he spoke English. I bought what I needed, resolved to consult the maid.

'I can do the bazar for you, Didi.'

It beat going out myself. For the basics, at least. She came with gram and dal and onions and rice. I looked at them.

'Can you cook?'

She didn't turn a hair. 'Yes, Didi.'

'What if...?'

It was settled in a matter of minutes. She'd prepare the evening meal, all I needed to do was warm it up.

Sachin was amused. 'If this is what she calls cooking, maybe we'd better find someone else.'

'It isn't her, it tasted fine when she left...'

The next day, the guard puffed and panted at the door. 'Delivery, Memsaab.'

A microwave? More alien to me than a stove. 'How the hell do you work this thing?' I asked, as we picked at our (delivered) chicken tandoori and naan.

'Have you read the instructions?'

'You do it.'

He did. He wanted to. It was a machine, he was the Man of the House. Armed with the last naan, a bowl of dal and piece of chicken, he set to work. When he was done, the naan could have served for shoe-leather, the dal was a pitted solid mass but the chicken was, well, edible. It took me two more dinners to achieve perfection.

'Ahh,' He said when I did, 'A hot, home-cooked meal, at last. What a wife!'

I resolved there and then, to learn. Dal and a basic veg curry. Nothing fancy.

*Garnish, if you will, with coriander leaves and chopped green chillies.*

It was a start. He tasted the results, declared them palatable, though not always.

Man does not live on rice and dal, vegetable and salad alone, meat is necessary, fish optional. My guides weren't Bengali so my concoctions weren't either.

We made friends in Delhi-Gurgaon-really. Susmita and her husband, Rohit, Anjali and Purshottam, Bobby and Anjan. Each and every one expatriated from somewhere else, cast up by the wave of corporate expansion sweeping the country. The tiny Marutis that had been the pride and joy overshadowed by giant four-wheel-drive Sumos, the stalls on Janpath cringing under the malls springing up. We revelled in the experience, burgers and drinks at the bars of five-star hotels. Dinners *al fresco* – our vocabularies were expanding faster than the menfolks' waistlines. And while they were at the office, we arranged to meet for coffee and tea, played with the new kitchen equipment they bought for us. Pressure cookers were old hat, toasters and mixers and blenders *passé*. Susmita acquired a bread-making machine from a US-returned distant cousin, Anjali a waffle-maker. When we tired of these, we went to the multiplex cinema, sat in the cool darkness, eating spicy snacks, drinking cola and oohing and aahing over the screen idols. Richard Gere was too pale, too grey, Shah Rukh Khan too delicious for words.

Sachin had to travel. 'Comes with the territory,' He said. Of course it did. I didn't think twice about it, barely two years with him and now he was away more often than he was around. C'est la vie. I'd tried taking up French, the Alliance Française, but it wasn't for me, even the social side of things. Too many earnest, arty types, might as well have been back in Calcutta, they wanted the language to deepen their souls. What is it about French that attracts these types? Susmita was doing German, everyone there was matter-of-fact, she said. They had direction, jobs, education, things concrete. Not plumbing the depths of their souls. I struggled through four weeks, dropped out.

Sachin came back from Hong Kong.

'Amazing!' he said.

I imagined it was, steel and glass and shiny modern metro.

'It's more than that. I'll take you some time.'

Like hell, he would, I thought, in my innocence. Yes, we were on the up and up – he was, at least – but wives didn't get to travel until you were higher up the food chain, so to speak. Bobby did, but Anjan was a Director. Family firm, it was true, but a Director all the same. She'd been to New York and London and Paris and Singapore.

'It's all the same, yaar. You go there, stay in hotels, go out for dinner, do some shopping. Taxis, yaar, you never need to meet the hoi pulao.' Anjan looked uncomfortable as she turned to him, 'Isn't it, darling? All the same, everywhere.'

'Not quite...'

They were an odd couple. Whatever he was at work – and he was Someone, the family firm was growing leaps and bounds – in his wife's presence he was a mouse. She walked all over him. I think that's why he liked visiting us; Sachin and Rohit and he and Purshottam got to disappear and talk shop, stocks and shares and property, mostly property, while Susmita, Anjali and I got to entertain Bobby. Which wasn't her real name of course, she wouldn't reveal the alternative.

'Bobby's good enough, yaar, why do you want more? If they'd asked me, I'd have told my parents.'

She was from Bombay, downright refused to call it Mumbai. 'Listen, yaar, I've been calling it Bombay since I was this high, why should I change now?' She flicked her perfectly trimmed hair back with a perfectly enamelled nail. 'Those buggers want to call it something else, they can.'

We all thought of it as Bombay too, so we didn't argue. Besides, she had presents for us all. Lipstick and perfume. 'All the rage in Paris, yaar. Got them in the magazines.' She said it with such confidence, we didn't dare ask how she got so much out of magazines. Or why. Then I remembered from my French class that the department stores in Paris were called 'magasins' so that's where she'd probably got them. If I'd stuck with the French classes...

'We were in this amazing place in New York, yaar.'

How I envied her, all the places she'd been. My Sachin had his head down and his eyes up but it was beyond the horizon then. He was collecting air miles but he didn't fly far enough, often enough. In a year he hadn't even collected enough to get me one way to Singapore.

'You could get off in Rangoon and walk the rest of the way,' Anjali laughed. She could see the funny side of things. Purshottam was corporate too but laid back and she, dark, plain and, deep down, homely, wasn't in a hurry to go anywhere. She enjoyed where she was and the vicarious pleasure of listening to Bobby.

'They have these consergies in New York, yaar, like durwans but better dressed. The manners they have, yaar!'

And we didn't ask her whether they were good or bad, these manners. It was enough to know they were different and she, one of us, had experienced them. It was amazing how casually she treated it all, she hadn't grown up in luxury or anything. In fact, her mother was, some whispered, Anglo-Indian, and she herself had been a secretary at a lawyer friend of Anjan's. He'd met her at the office and been smitten. Really smitten, not just hungry smitten, taken her out and gone to ask her parents' permission for her hand.

'Did you ever hear anything so romantic?' Susmita swooned.

Not off screen, we hadn't. Bobby didn't tell us about it, though, Anjan told the men. 'The boys,' Bobby called them. She could. Susmita and I tried saying it too but it didn't sound right, we sounded like we were trying to sound like Bobby. Which we couldn't, we weren't Bombay, we weren't Bobby. She even got away with wearing a dress to a New Year's party. Jeans, slacks we could carry off but not dresses. Even if we knew better than to call them 'frocks'. Yet there was Bobby, in a swirly red and green silk number right out of the pages of a magazine, the paper type.

'You like it, yaar?' We nodded dumbly. Anjan smiled his timid smile and sidled off to join the other men. They'd got a book of cocktails and he'd brought back bitters from his travels. They were mixing pink gins for us and Martinis for themselves. Anjan had brought olives and they were having fun spearing them.

'Boys!' Bobby rolled her eyes. We went out on the balcony, Bobby lit a cigarette and the rest of us tried not to look impressed.

'What's it really like?' Anjali asked. 'All those wonderful shops and cars...'

'Like Bombay, yaar, only better. You should see Tiffany's.'

We travelled in her stories, never knowing what to believe and what not to. Did men really kiss in New York bars? And did black men really have white girlfriends? What did people do at cafés in Vienna? Was Switzerland like The Sound of Music? Or was that Austria?

It didn't matter. 'Snow everywhere, yaar. Ruins your shoes. And the furs!'

I'd never seen real fur, not off an animal at any rate. I wasn't too sure I'd like to have it round my neck but I liked hearing about it.

Susmita bought a new cookbook. Inspired by Bobby's travels, constrained by Anjali and Purshottam's vegetarianism, we invented.

Bobby found it hilarious. 'Mashed potatoes desi style?' But Sachin had seconds. All the men did. While Susmita and

I glowed and served mango kulfi (shop bought) for dessert. Bobby liked it too, even though she forgot to say so. I'm sure she did. She didn't say she didn't like it, did she?

Sachin went again. Singapore was it? Maybe Dubai. Or Abu Dhabi. For all I knew, it might as well have been Timbuktu. Business was booming, there was a future in call centres. The firm had three serving American banks in Bangalore already and was negotiating with another. Their regional office was in charge, Sachin was the negotiator.

'They dial a number in New York or Houston or LA or wherever and they get our kids in Bangalore on the line! They don't even notice the difference.'

This was in the days before enough Yanks started complaining, before Sachin saw better prospects in outsourcing. Off he flew, leaving me to experiment. Anjali's influence in the kitchen was strong, curry leaves had become fundamental. I took mincemeat, made it with a twist of my own. Susmita liked it, so did Sachin when, back from his travels, he got to taste it.

'They hardly bargained,' he crowed, 'And we'd just doubled the price!'

The girls and boys at the centres didn't get any more, of course, but they did get careers. Ten were promoted to floor managers. It wasn't a grade anyone had expected to exist but there it was suddenly. Six boys and four girls. Susmita wasn't sure whether it was a good idea.

'These people, they haven't been to college, have they?'

'Actually,' Sachin said, 'They have. All BAs, BScs, each and every one.'

'But not from *good* colleges...'

Bobby was having none of it. 'What's all this shop talking, yaar? Are we here to party or what?'

We were there to party, we all agreed. Susmita had arranged a picnic out at Damdama. Her cook and driver packed the Sumo with food, Anjan filled all the extra space with beer, rum and whisky.

'Maasti!' Purshottam sang, even though he was very nearly teetotal. One rum and coke was enough to bring him out in a sweat and a beer put him to sleep faster than gripe water did a baby.

Our convoy bounced along, Anjan, Purshottam and Sachin in the lead Gypsy, us women and Rohit behind in the Ambassador, and the Sumo with Susmita's cook, maid and driver bringing up the rear.

'This is great, isn't it?' Anjali giggled as we dodged round another line of lumbering lorries.

'Nothing like the seaside in Bombay,' Bobby said. 'You should do that sometime, yaar. It's supermagnificent!'

At the resort (why had we brought our own supplies?), the men went off to try the manly activities while we womenfolk organised the cook and maid. The Sumo yielded up a long table, the 'cottage' (a grandly titled hut), provided chairs.

'Plate leyaao, glass leyaao...' Susmita was in her element, organising her staff. It suddenly struck me that of all the four couples, we were the only one with no permanent staff. There was the maid who came every morning, stayed till nearly lunchtime, the driver who came and went with the car, the building's durwans, but no live-in staff. We didn't have the space, really, the servants' quarters allotted to our flat had been sublet by the previous occupant and the owners hadn't bothered to reclaim it.

The men came back, flushed from exertion, thirsty.

'Beer!' Sachin commanded and Rohit obliged, flicking caps from bottles with practised ease.

'Aaah, this is the life, isn't it?' Purshottam beamed, his exercise glow growing brighter as the beer took effect.

'Good, isn't it, yaar?' Bobby said, waving her gin and tonic. 'All we need is the sea.'

'Get over it,' Rohit said, 'This is the mid-point of the sub-continent, the sea isn't going to get here in a million years.'

'Once upon a time,' Anjan said dreamily, 'The Himalayas were under water and the whole landmass floated here to meet Asia. Wonderful, when you think of it, isn't it?'

'And it's pushing its way up and up and we'll all end up at the North Pole one day,' Sachin chuckled, 'That took millions of years. Right now, it isn't going anywhere fast!'

'But the country is,' Rohit said. 'Imagine this twenty years ago?'

'Bugger twenty years ago, yaar,' Bobby said, 'Let's enjoy today!'

The food came, tandoori chicken, aloo mattar, peas gobi, chola bhatura and salads for the vegetarians, dal and raita and ice cream and more to drink. Anjali stuck to cola but Susmita and I joined Bobby in gin and T's, as she called them.

'There's a cocktail called A Long Screw Up Against a Wall,' Rohit was saying.

Anjali's brow furrowed. 'What's special about a screw against a wall?'

We all laughed at her image of ironmongery rusting against brickwork. Dear, dear Anjali, innocent of the innocents.

Bobby, Susmita, Anjali, me. Anjan, Rohit, Purshottam, Sachin. The times we had together.

It didn't come as a shock but it did come as a surprise. Sachin and I hardly ever found time to talk; he was at work most of the time and I filled my days with outings with the girls and experimenting in the kitchen. He'd been offered a job. A new company, a new direction. The prospects were

'Amazing! Six months here and then...'

Then what? Transfer. Where? 'Who knows? The world is our oyster!'

I told the girls.

'Congratulations!' Susmita said.

'Good for you, yaar,' Bobby said, inspecting her nails for chipped enamel (I don't know why she did, there never was any), 'You might get to go somewhere civilised for a change.'

Unimpressed to begin with, she was now thoroughly bored. 'Tandoori, that's all that's here,' she complained. 'No culture!' She was from Bombay, after all. Melting pot, not capital blot.

'You'll keep in touch, won't you?' Anjali worried.

'Of course I will,' I assured her. Susmita was my best friend but it was Anjali I felt most tender towards. Plain, simple Anjali with her housewife looks and clothes. No matter how hard she tried, she looked like she needed middle age to come into her own as a homely matron.

Bobby yawned, her beautiful, languid yawn. 'I'm trying to get Anjan to move but he won't.'

'He told me the family needs him here,' Anjali said loyally. She always stood up for the husbands.

'The family doesn't need anyone anywhere, yaar,' Bobby said. 'They just don't have the imagination to do anything differently.'

Susmita and I exchanged glances. That was patently unfair; Rohit and Sachin often went into raptures when the other two couples weren't around about Anjan's family. They were 'growing' the business like no-one had ever before. Except, perhaps, the big ones…it didn't matter that others were, what mattered was that his family was. The sky was the limit. Anjan's uncle had taken the petrol dealership and diversified. And how! Computer supplies first, then television parts. Now they were talking to a Japanese firm about setting up a subsidiary. All systems go, in other words. That's how Sachin saw it.

'If only I could get them to take me on,' he said wistfully. But he didn't really want that, it would have meant Anjan would've become his boss and that'd have been the end of all of us. It was better being his friend, more of the glory rubbed off that way.

Sachin broke the news to his employers. They made a desultory token offer.

'A temporary promotion?!' he'd exclaimed, 'You can do better than that!'

'Singhal is leaving in two months for Head Office. If things go well when you're Acting…'

'That's conditional.'

'Yes. We want to be certain.'

'That's not the way others feel.'

'They have their ways, we ours.'

'Meaning?'

'Can I be frank? Good, well, I think they're gambling. Face it, if you go, you'll be too.'

'Staying on is more of a gamble for me.'

'You know us, we know you.'

'Not well enough, apparently.'

'Well enough to trust you with a trial.'

They weren't really keen, it was plain to see. 'Their loss, my gain,' Sachin shrugged.

They threw a farewell for him. Meal at a five-star. Wives not invited, it was politeness, rather than anything else. A couple of people from Accounts came and one from Human Resources, which used to be Personnel. None could stay, they had other appointments.

Back home earlier than he expected, earlier than in months, he poured himself a stiff whisky, went out on the balcony. 'After all those years you'd think a few more would show up,' he grumbled.

'It doesn't matter, does it?'

We looked at each other, saw each other silhouetted against the bright-lit towers, beyond a sky of twinkling stars. In the near distance, the sound of traffic.

'Cheers,' he said, raising his glass to me. I raised my cup of tea and I smiled at him.

# The ingredients of *A simple recipe*

Growing up in India in the 1970s and 80s was to experience a society that felt, in many ways, static. Almost in limbo, moon shots and television happened in the newspapers and on the radio while the world we inhabited went on seemingly as it always had. The ubiquitous cars, the Ambassador, based on the Morris Oxford, and the Premier, originally a Fiat, gained fins, changed the shape of their headlights, provided diesel options and that was about it. Digital watches came from 'the West' and were much prized; electronic calculators were objects of envy. Families kept their refrigerators in their living rooms, carefully draped with cloth, like the televisions which served not just the household but the neighbours. It was a world of, at most, incremental change, even when I finished school and went on to do a degree, I couldn't imagine anything radical happening. Other than politically, as the fortunes of parties rose and fell. Or even politically, really, the Emergency (1975 to 1977 when Indira Gandhi suspended the Constitution and Parliament, the closest India came to dictatorship) apart, the same individuals, though in different parties, contested, won and lost. Then, cautiously at first, soon with increasing speed, things did begin to change. Nothing to do with the fall of the Berlin Wall, but with the economy 'opening up' in the 1980s and 90s. People, especially the middle classes, were being affected. Not just by shiny new gadgets; their prospects and aspirations were being radically modified. No longer were they looking forward to lives that extended, slightly changed, those of their parents, they were having to adapt to a whole new set of circumstances, new opportunities and futures. There was a story in it, I felt, about someone who changes personally as the world around does. The question was: who? I wanted a character who is drawn into things, unwilling, surprised perhaps, but not resisting, adapting instead. I toyed with several ideas, of career men and people rising out of poverty but the one that appealed most, that ticked the boxes, was that of a girl becoming a woman. A girl-next-door drawn into the new ways, sucked inexorably into new ways and discovering herself as things change around her. She, I felt, could tell the story herself.

Yes, herself. Because first person narration entices the reader into trusting and identifying with the character, especially if, as in this case, the character is naïve, vulnerable. From the point of view of writing, however, it is tricky, an illusion that needs to be nurtured. It is, after all, inherently false. In reality, stories are told with the knowledge that the narrator has at the time of the telling, with post-event interpretation and hindsight infusing the recounting of all past events. But in this kind of storytelling, the narrator has to be almost innocent at the outset, developing in awareness and complexity as the story unfolds. Knowledge, in other words, has to be consistent with the time of narration, with the narrator only communicating what she (or he) might know at the time, not what she will or might know or understand later. This had some immediate effects. For instance, I originally wrote that the narrator discovers later that Bobby's 'magazines' are, in fact, French *grands magasins*, department stores. But at the time she has no obvious way of knowing, especially since she has recently withdrawn from French lessons. Since I did not want to allow her to use knowledge she acquires later, I changed things so that her understanding occurred closer to the time of experience, having her remember from her lessons. I could, of course, have allowed her future self and knowledge to intrude but that would have been giving the 'future' away. And just then, I wanted to keep the focus very much on the character as she is, not on what is to become of her.

Consistency in knowledge apart, there needed to be consistency in character. Both in her and in those around her. There was a useful tool at my disposal: prejudice. People are, after all, essentially prejudiced; they compartmentalise others in order to understand them. In India, awareness of one's identity (or proclaimed identity and awareness of it) is commonplace; people identify as being of community A, from city B, school C and so on. This may seem petty but it is real, and, while working on the characters, projecting their prejudices (Bobby's alleged Anglo-Indian roots, Bombay/Mumbai's feeling of cultural superiority over Delhi), allowed me to tease out details of their world and their personalities. I know that everything I drew upon and put in may not be accessible to all readers, but those details are essential in making the characters individuals, so Sachin's envy of Anjan and his family business defines Sachin as much as, and perhaps more than, it defines Anjan.

My next consideration was the structure and choice of detail. This is the beginning, the introductory chapter and, as such, has several purposes. To establish the scene, to establish the characters and to propose the tensions in the story to come when, seeking her own identity, she uses the culinary skills she develops to rid herself of her husband. I could have begun by saying 'this is India, late 1980s', I could even have just provided a date and place, as some do. I wanted, however, for all this to reveal itself. The character, the girl-woman herself, was my most important element and for her to preface her story with a statement of place or time felt artificial. She is, in a sense, thinking the story to herself, not actually narrating it to anyone. I also wanted to skip a large part of her life, the period before her marriage, except a few telling details to establish her background. So I was selective, juxtaposing traditional elements – the marriage arrangements, the horoscopes – with her personal tastes – the American book of horoscopes, the English novels, the private use of American slang to distinguish the pairs of parents – to create a sense of people who live on a cultural border, sometimes tipping one way, at others another. So while the women are articulate and educated, they accept their traditional roles of being supportive wives. Similarly, they expect their servants to be traditional while they themselves acquire the labour-saving devices and take up cooking because it is now fashionable. Where they might once have been wary of cooking, even almost been discouraged from it, as the protagonist was, as devices appear on the market and are the thing to have, they buy them in. Initially they are just toys but they insinuate themselves, becoming, in their own peculiar way, liberating, allowing the narrator to express herself, awakening her to the possibility that she doesn't have to follow the old recipes, she can make up her own.

Another important idea for this opening chapter was that of moving the protagonist from her 'safe zone', the world as she had known it, she had grown up in. I began by establishing the 'normality' of the world as she experienced it; she insists on the expectedness of all that happens to her, the choice of partner, the wedding itself, the move to her in-laws. Once that was in place, she was ready to be moved on. Which her husband's career choice allowed. After all, I didn't want her to be hankering after change, I wanted her to discover that there was another world, a world in which she can invent herself. When Sachin is transferred, opportunity presents itself, the new place is hers in that it isn't the family's. Even the most obvious, expected details of life are upset. There is no market nearby, she has to use a shopping mall and the local rickshaws attempt to cheat her. There is little for her to relate to, details are significantly different: the maid, from an underprivileged background, who ought to be overwhelmed, has the measure of the area so is in control in a way her mistress is not. And Bobby, neither from here, Delhi, or there, Calcutta, is a catalyst; by being from the glamorous city, Bombay, she embodies all that the other women aren't. She smokes, drinks, travels, wears dresses. The others don't so much aspire to be her, they marvel at her. But their engagement with her is also traditional, there is an underlying snobbery, she is seen as outside the norm, of Anglo-Indian parentage and reputedly once a secretary, now with a husband 'above her station'. She is an important figure, very much herself, mangling the foreign words with the confidence of someone who feels at home in places unimaginable to her peers. She is also a foil; the other women need her because she shows how different things can be while they play more traditional roles, representing alternative lives for my protagonist. Anjali is a plain but clever housewife who knows her place yet is capable of holding her own if necessary, while Susmita is the narrator's parallel, so similar that they cannot actually be close friends. And because, in the end, it is to be different that the narrator craves, the narrator is drawn more to Bobby and Anjali, not to emulate them but because they provide the ingredients, the stimulus, for her new self.

Next, to fill in the picture, to provide the immediate tension, I drew the men. Seeing themselves as the engineers of the new world, they revel in the freedom it allows, yet are intellectually unengaged, ignorant, blind. They travel and drink, buy expensive cars without a thought; for them opportunity is a given and all they need do is help themselves. Loudly fraternal, they are also traditional, never imagining that their spouses might want or develop into something other than the slightly adapted roles that have been imagined for them. Even Bobby fulfils that role; she is just sufficiently exotic yet, at the same time, of an exoticism that they recognise, one that understands the rules and plays within them, knowing when to dress one way, where a woman can smoke, drink, dance and, at the same time, able to accept the other wives, their lives apparently so different from hers, without question. The men, meanwhile, are happy with the way things are, their horizons are expanding, they feel that the new ways empower them, that they are in control. It doesn't occur to them that things might be more complex, that the freedom they are now able to afford for themselves and their wives might be affecting their lives in unexpected ways. On the one hand, they, like the women, go along with traditional marriage and a parallel liberal perspective of a woman's duties and of partnership and, on the other, they are oblivious to the fact that such changes in lifestyle are bound to affect their partners. This produces the fundamental tension in the story: rather than being oppressive, the men represent a benevolent yet blind society, one that, while it means no harm, lacks the imagination to respond to the women. It is a state of inertia that the narrator is to rebel against. In this first chapter, while she is not rebelling yet, she is beginning to experience the restrictions that remain in a benevolent 'tradition' embodied by the men, and the seeds of the idea that there might be an alternative are being planted.

It wasn't all plain sailing, of course; along the line I also cut back on material. Most obviously, in this case, on recipes, traces of which remain. The fact that my narrator came from an 'enlightened' family and didn't know how to cook was crucial to my story so I set about collecting and writing down recipes to fill in the thread, organising them in terms of how difficult they might seem to someone who had (probably) spent time as a child around the kitchen but none in it. Someone with taste buds and a latent knowledge to be gradually awakened (like her knowledge of herself). It was a task I enjoyed but it soon took on a life of its own, filling page after page. I hesitated, realising that Isabel Allende's *Aphrodite*, which I had read not long before and which blended narrative, recipes and art, wasn't really a model that was working for me. My narrative was getting lost among the ingredients and instruction, the recipes weren't actually combining with storytelling, the food was overwhelming the story. I took a deep breath and did what a cook must: trimmed away the excess. Without mercy, as with a sharp knife. And, when it was done, I was relieved to see that the narrative had picked up pace, the characters were responding to each other better, and their world and ideas were more readily accessible.

And thus I had it, India changing, as seen and experienced by a woman coming to realise that things don't have to be the way they are. The stage is set.

# References

Allende, I., *Aphrodite* (New York: Harper Flamingo, 1995)

Anchevski, Z., *Strategy of defeat: selected poems 1984–2000* trans. S. Sen (Skopje: Jugoreklam, 2000)

Anon, *Pearl*, ed. E.V. Gordon (London: OUP, 1953)

Babel, I., *1920 diary*, trans. H.T. Willets (New Haven: Yale University Press, 2002)

Babel, I., *The collected stories of Isaac Babel*, trans. P. Constantine, ed. N. Babel (New York: W.W. Norton & Company, 2002)

Blanchot, M., *The gaze of Orpheus and other literary essays*, trans. L. Davis (Barrytown, NY: Station Hill Press, 1981)

Breathnach, C., *An Fear Marbh* (Inverin: Cló Iar-Chonnachta, 1998)

Breathnach, C., *Chiaroscuro* (Dublin: Coiscéim, 2006)

Breathnach, C., *'Dánta' agus dánta eile* (Dublin: Coiscéim, 2011)

Brontë, E., *Wuthering Heights* (London: Penguin, 2009 [1848])

Carey, P., *Parrot and Olivier in America* (Camberwell, Victoria: Hamish Hamilton, 2009)

Cartier-Bresson, H., 'HCB à la question', *Photo* no.144 (Paris: Sept 1979)

Clendinnen, I., 'The history question: who owns the past?', *Quarterly Essay 23* (2006), 1–72

Coleridge, S. T., *Collected Letters II*, ed. E.L. Griggs (London: OUP, 1956)

Davidson, D., 'Knowing one's own mind', *Mind and cognition: an anthology*, ed. W. G. Lycan, (Oxford: Blackwell, 1999)

de Paor, L., 'Contemporary poetry in Irish: 1940–2000', *The Cambridge history of Irish literature*, two vols: eds. M. Kelleher and P. O'Leary (Cambridge: Cambridge University Press, 2006), vol II (1890–2000)

de Sola Pinto, V., 'D. H. Lawrence: letter-writer and craftsman in verse', *Renaissance and Modern Studies* 1 (1957), 5–34

Donaghy, M., *Safest* (London: Picador, 2005)

Douglas, K., *The Complete Poems* (London: Faber, 1978)

Draycott, J., *Pearl: a translation* (Manchester: Carcanet Press, 2011)

Frost, R., *Complete Poems* (New York: Henry Holt, 1949)

Gaiman, N., 'On writing American Gods', *The Guardian* (London: Guardian News, 2 Sept 2011)

Garner, A., *Strandloper* (London: Random House, 1997)

Garner, A., *The voice that thunders* (London: Harvill Press, 1999)

Gaskin, I.M., *Ina May's guide to childbirth* (New York: Bantam, 2003)

Gittings, R. (ed.) *Letters of John Keats* (Oxford: OUP, 1970)

Gross, P., *Changes of address: poems 1980–98* (Tarset: Bloodaxe, 2001)

Gross, P., *Deep field* (Tarset: Bloodaxe, 2011)

Gross, P., 'Giving houseroom to our waifs and strays: questions for the writing workshop and the writing self', *Creative Writing: Teaching Theory and Practice* 2:1 (2010) 33–40

Gross, P., *Off road to everywhere* (London: Salt, 2010)

Gross, P., 'Then again what do I know: reflections on reflection in Creative Writing', *The writer in the academy: creative interfrictions*, ed. R. Marggraf Turley (Cambridge: English Association/Boydell & Brewer, 2011)

Herbert, W. and Hollis, M. (eds.), *Strong words: modern poets on modern poetry* (Tarset: Bloodaxe Books, 2000)

Jones, D., preface to *The anathemata* (London: Faber, 1952)

Joyce, J., *Dubliners*, ed. J. Johnson (Oxford: OUP, 2000)

Lawrence, D. H., *Complete poems vol. I*, eds. V. de Sola Pinto and W. Roberts (London: Heinemann, 1964)

Lowell, R., *Day by day* (New York: Farrar, 1977)

McGahern, J., *That they may face the rising sun* (London: Faber, 2002)

Miller, A., *The ancestor game* (Sydney: Allen & Unwin, 1992)

Morgan, E., 'The Poet's Voice and Craft', *The poet's voice and craft*, ed. C. McCully, (Manchester: Carcanet Press, 1994)

Murray, L., *A defence of poetry* (Rotterdam: Poetry International Festival Lecture, 1998)

Nic Eoin, M., 'Colm Breathnach', *Filíocht Chomhaimseartha na Gaeilge*, ed. R. Ní Fhrighil (Dublin: Cois Life, 2010)

Ní Dhuibhne, É., 'Why would anyone write in Irish?', *'Who needs Irish?': Reflections on the importance of the Irish language today*, ed. C. Mac Murchaidh (Dublin: Veritas Publications, 2004)

Ó Bruadair, D., 'D'aithle na bhFileadh', Duanaire *Dháibhidh Uí Bhruadair* Part III, ed. J. Mac Erlean (London: Irish Texts Society, 1917) (Line quoted translated by J. Mac Erlean)

Ó Muirthile, L., 'Offshore on land – poetry in Irish now', *A new view of the Irish language*, ed. C. Nic Pháidín and S. Ó Cearnaigh, (Dublin: Cois Life, 2008)

Pitcher, J. (ed.), *The Arden Shakespeare – The winter's tale* (London: Methuen, 2010)

Proust, M., *Du côté de chez Swann*, eds. P. Clarac and A. Ferré, (Paris: Gallimard, 1954)

Rilke, R.M., *Selected poetry of Rainer Maria Rilke*, trans. S. Mitchell (New York: Random House, 1982)

Shapcott, J., *My life asleep* (Oxford: OUP, 1998)

Steger, J., 'It's a risky business', *Sydney Morning Herald, Books* (Pyrmont: Sydney Morning Herald, 25–27 April, 2008)

Stevens, W., *Harmonium* (New York: Knopf, 1923)

Stevens, W., *Opus posthumous*, ed. S.F. Morse (London: Faber, 1959)

Ward, R., *Beautiful Kate* (Newtown Films, 2009)

Winton, T., *Cloudstreet* (Ringwood, Victoria: Penguin, 1991)

Woolf, V., 'Mr Bennett and Mrs. Brown', *Collected essays vol. 1*, ed. L. Woolf, (London: Hogarth, 1966)

Wordsworth, W., *Poems in two volumes (1807): vol II*, ed. J.O. Hayden (Harmondsworth: Penguin, 1977)